Voice of Praise

A Collection of Standard Hymns and Gospel Songs Published For Use in the Worship Hour, Sunday Schools, Young People's Meetings, Evangelistic Services, and all Christian Work and Worship

B. B. McKINNEY

Music Editor

PRINTED IN ROUND AND SHAPED NOTES

BROADMAN PRESS — NASHVILLE, TENNESSEE

Copyright 1947, by Broadman Press

PRINTED AND BOUND IN THE UNITED STATES OF AMERICA
25KP453

FOREWORD

VOICE OF PRAISE has been compiled to meet the demand for a book of praise suited to the needs of all departments of church work and worship where good enthusiastic singing is most desired.

VOICE OF PRAISE contains an unusual variety of old standard hymns and gospel songs which have long been endeared to the Christian heart and a number of new songs and choruses which will also undoubtedly soon sing themselves into the hearts of all who use them.

A group of responsive readings is included. They have been selected from both the Old and New Testaments for use in the regular worship services.

VOICE OF PRAISE is sent forth with the fullest confidence that it will fulfil every requirement of church life.

"Let the people praise thee, O God; let all the people praise thee."

BROADMAN PRESS
T. L. Holcomb
Executive Secretary

Doxology

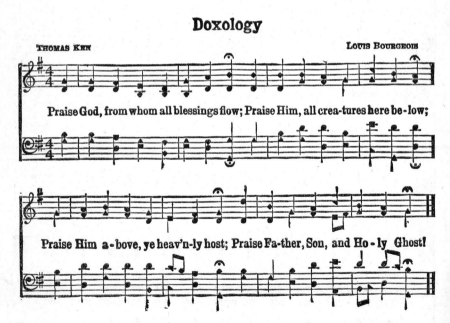

VOICE OF PRAISE

1

Crown Him with Many Crowns

DIADEMATA

MATTHEW BRIDGES

G. J. ELVEY

1. Crown Him with man - y crowns, The Lamb up - on His throne;
2. Crown Him the Lord of love; Be - hold His hands and side,
3. Crown Him the Lord of life! Who tri-umphed o'er the grave;

Hark! how the heaven-ly an-them drowns All mu - sic but its own:
Rich wounds, yet vis - i - ble a - bove, In beau - ty glo - ri - fied:
Who rose vic - to - rious to the strife For those He came to save:

A - wake, my soul, and sing Of Him who died for thee, And
No an - gel in the sky Can ful - ly bear that sight, But
His glo - ries now we sing, Who died and rose on high; Who

hail Him as thy match-less King Thro' all e - ter - ni - ty.
down-ward bends his burn - ing eye At mys - ter - ies so bright.
died e - ter - nal life to bring, And lives that death may die.

Praise Him! Praise Him!

FANNY J. CROSBY

CHESTER G. ALLEN

1. Praise Him! praise Him! Je-sus, our bless-ed Re-deem-er! Sing, O Earth, His
2. Praise Him! praise Him! Je-sus, our bless-ed Re-deem-er! For our sins He
3. Praise Him! praise Him! Je-sus, our bless-ed Re-deem-er! Heavenly por-tals

won-der-ful love pro-claim! Hail Him! hail Him! highest archangels in glo-ry;
suffered, and bled, and died; He our Rock, our hope of e-ter-nal sal-va-tion,
loud with ho-san-nas ring! Je-sus, Sav-iour, reigneth for-ev-er and ev-er;

Strength and hon-or give to His ho-ly name! Like a shep-herd, Je-sus will
Hail Him! hail Him! Je-sus the Cru-ci-fied. Sound His prais-es! Je-sus who
Crown Him! crown Him! Prophet, and Priest, and King! Christ is com-ing! o-ver the

REFRAIN

guard His children, In His arms He carries them all day long:
bore our sor-rows, Love unbounded, wonderful, deep and strong: Praise Him! praise Him!
world vic-to-rious, Power and glo-ry un-to the Lord be-long:

tell of His ex-cel-lent greatness: Praise Him! praise Him! ev-er in joy-ful song!

3 Blessed Assurance

FANNY J. CROSBY

Mrs. J. F. KNAPP

1. Bless-ed as - sur - ance, Je - sus is mine! Oh, what a fore - taste of
2. Per - fect sub - mis - sion, per - fect de - light, Vi - sions of rap - ture now
3. Per - fect sub - mis - sion, all is at rest, I in my Sav - iour am

glo - ry di - vine! Heir of sal - va - tion, pur - chase of God,
burst on my sight; An - gels de - scend-ing, bring from a - bove
hap - py and blest; Watch-ing and wait - ing, look - ing a - bove,

CHORUS

Born of His Spir - it, washed in His blood.
Ech - oes of mer - cy, whis - pers of love. This is my sto - ry,
Filled with His good - ness, lost in His love.

this is my song, Prais-ing my Sav - iour all the day long; This is my

sto - ry, this is my song, Prais-ing my Sav - iour all the day long.

4

Love Divine

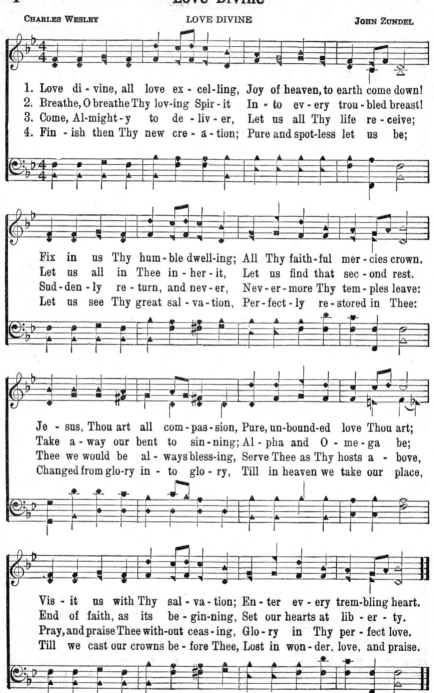

CHARLES WESLEY   LOVE DIVINE   JOHN ZUNDEL

1. Love di - vine, all love ex - cel-ling, Joy of heaven, to earth come down!
2. Breathe, O breathe Thy lov-ing Spir - it In - to ev - ery trou - bled breast!
3. Come, Al-might-y to de - liv - er, Let us all Thy life re - ceive;
4. Fin - ish then Thy new cre - a - tion; Pure and spot-less let us be;

Fix in us Thy hum - ble dwell-ing; All Thy faith-ful mer - cies crown.
Let us all in Thee in - her - it, Let us find that sec - ond rest.
Sud - den - ly re - turn, and nev - er, Nev - er-more Thy tem - ples leave:
Let us see Thy great sal - va - tion, Per - fect - ly re - stored in Thee:

Je - sus, Thou art all com - pas - sion, Pure, un-bound-ed love Thou art;
Take a - way our bent to sin-ning; Al - pha and O - me - ga be;
Thee we would be al - ways bless-ing, Serve Thee as Thy hosts a - bove,
Changed from glo-ry in - to glo - ry, Till in heaven we take our place,

Vis - it us with Thy sal - va - tion; En - ter ev - ery trem-bling heart.
End of faith, as its be - gin-ning, Set our hearts at lib - er - ty.
Pray, and praise Thee with-out ceas-ing, Glo - ry in Thy per - fect love.
Till we cast our crowns be - fore Thee, Lost in won - der, love, and praise.

5 Jesus Saves

PRISCILLA J. OWENS

WM. J. KIRKPATRICK

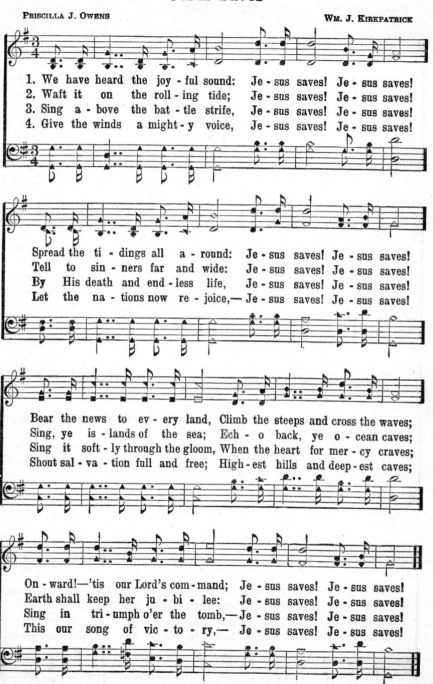

1. We have heard the joy - ful sound: Je - sus saves! Je - sus saves!
2. Waft it on the roll - ing tide; Je - sus saves! Je - sus saves!
3. Sing a - bove the bat - tle strife, Je - sus saves! Je - sus saves!
4. Give the winds a might - y voice, Je - sus saves! Je - sus saves!

Spread the ti - dings all a - round: Je - sus saves! Je - sus saves!
Tell to sin - ners far and wide: Je - sus saves! Je - sus saves!
By His death and end - less life, Je - sus saves! Je - sus saves!
Let the na - tions now re - joice,— Je - sus saves! Je - sus saves!

Bear the news to ev - ery land, Climb the steeps and cross the waves;
Sing, ye is - lands of the sea; Ech - o back, ye o - cean caves;
Sing it soft - ly through the gloom, When the heart for mer - cy craves;
Shout sal - va - tion full and free; High - est hills and deep - est caves;

On - ward!—'tis our Lord's com - mand; Je - sus saves! Je - sus saves!
Earth shall keep her ju - bi - lee: Je - sus saves! Je - sus saves!
Sing in tri - umph o'er the tomb,— Je - sus saves! Je - sus saves!
This our song of vic - to - ry,— Je - sus saves! Je - sus saves!

6 I Am Thine, O Lord

FANNY J. CROSBY

W. H. DOANE

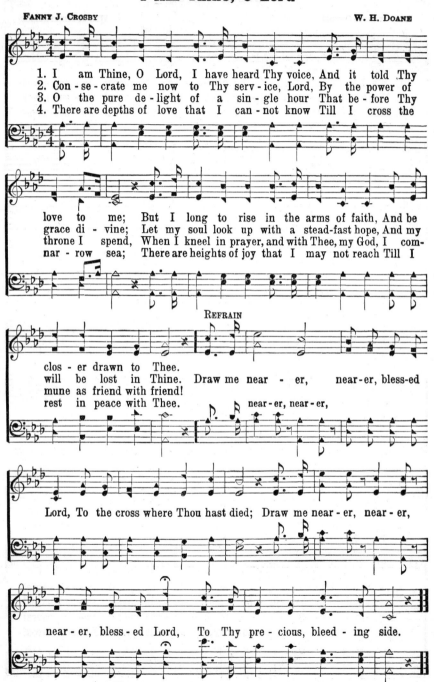

1. I am Thine, O Lord, I have heard Thy voice, And it told Thy
2. Con - se - crate me now to Thy serv - ice, Lord, By the power of
3. O the pure de - light of a sin - gle hour That be - fore Thy
4. There are depths of love that I can - not know Till I cross the

love to me; But I long to rise in the arms of faith, And be
grace di - vine; Let my soul look up with a stead-fast hope, And my
throne I spend, When I kneel in prayer, and with Thee, my God, I com-
nar - row sea; There are heights of joy that I may not reach Till I

Refrain

clos - er drawn to Thee.
will be lost in Thine. Draw me near - er, near - er, bless-ed
mune as friend with friend! near - er, near - er,
rest in peace with Thee.

Lord, To the cross where Thou hast died; Draw me near - er, near - er,

near - er, bless - ed Lord, To Thy pre - cious, bleed - ing side.

7. We've a Story to Tell

COLIN STERNE

H. E. NICHOL

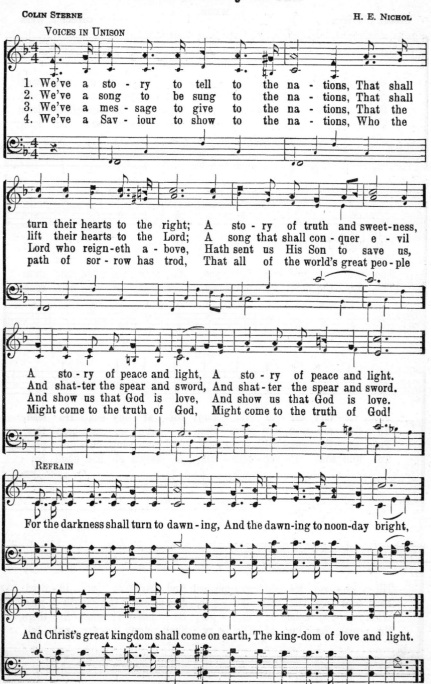

VOICES IN UNISON

1. We've a sto - ry to tell to the na - tions, That shall
2. We've a song to be sung to the na - tions, That shall
3. We've a mes - sage to give to the na - tions, That the
4. We've a Sav - iour to show to the na - tions, Who the

turn their hearts to the right; A sto - ry of truth and sweet-ness,
lift their hearts to the Lord; A song that shall con - quer e - vil
Lord who reign-eth a - bove, Hath sent us His Son to save us,
path of sor - row has trod, That all of the world's great peo - ple

A sto - ry of peace and light, A sto - ry of peace and light.
And shat - ter the spear and sword, And shat - ter the spear and sword.
And show us that God is love, And show us that God is love.
Might come to the truth of God, Might come to the truth of God!

REFRAIN

For the darkness shall turn to dawn - ing, And the dawn-ing to noon-day bright,

And Christ's great kingdom shall come on earth, The king-dom of love and light.

Stand Up, Stand Up for Jesus

WEBB

GEORGE DUFFIELD   GEORGE J. WEBB

1. Stand up, stand up for Je - sus, Ye sol - diers of the cross!
2. Stand up, stand up for Je - sus, The trump - et call o - bey;
3. Stand up, stand up for Je - sus, Stand in His strength a - lone;
4. Stand up, stand up for Je - sus, The strife will not be long;

Lift high His roy - al ban - ner, It must not suf - fer loss:
Forth to the might - y con - flict, In this His glo - rious day:
The arm of flesh will fail you, Ye dare not trust your own:
This day, the noise of bat - tle, The next, the vic - tor's song:

From vic - tory un - to vic - tory, His ar - my shall He lead,
Ye that are men, now serve Him, A - gainst un - num-bered foes;
Put on the gos - pel ar - mor, And, watch-ing un - to prayer,
To him that o - ver - com - eth, A crown of life shall be;

Till ev - ery foe is van-quished And Christ is Lord in - deed.
Your cour - age rise with dan - ger, And strength to strength op-pose.
Where du - ty calls, or dan - ger, Be nev - er want - ing there.
He with the King of Glo - ry Shall reign e - ter - nal - ly!

Onward, Christian Soldiers

SABINE BARING-GOULD ST. GERTRUDE ARTHUR SULLIVAN

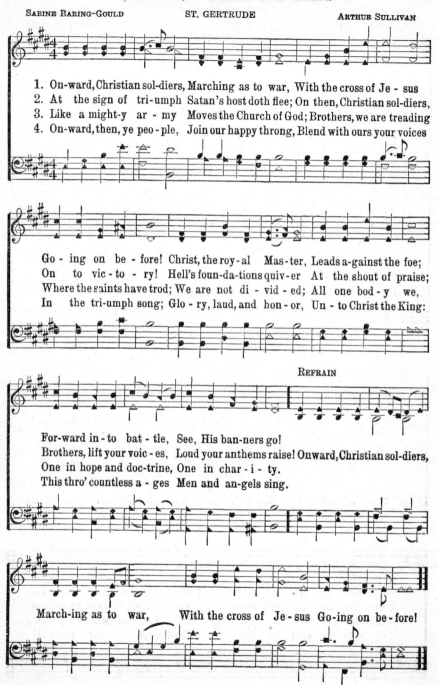

1. On-ward, Christian sol-diers, Marching as to war, With the cross of Je - sus
2. At the sign of tri-umph Satan's host doth flee; On then, Christian sol-diers,
3. Like a might-y ar - my Moves the Church of God; Brothers, we are treading
4. On-ward, then, ye peo - ple, Join our happy throng, Blend with ours your voices

Go - ing on be - fore! Christ, the roy-al Mas-ter, Leads a-gainst the foe;
On to vic - to - ry! Hell's foun-da-tions quiv-er At the shout of praise;
Where the saints have trod; We are not di - vid - ed; All one bod-y we,
In the tri-umph song; Glo - ry, laud, and hon - or, Un - to Christ the King:

REFRAIN

For-ward in - to bat - tle, See, His ban-ners go!
Brothers, lift your voic - es, Loud your anthems raise! Onward, Christian sol-diers,
One in hope and doc-trine, One in char - i - ty.
This thro' countless a - ges Men and an-gels sing.

March-ing as to war, With the cross of Je - sus Go-ing on be - fore!

The Banner of the Cross

D. W. WHITTLE   JAMES McGRANAHAN

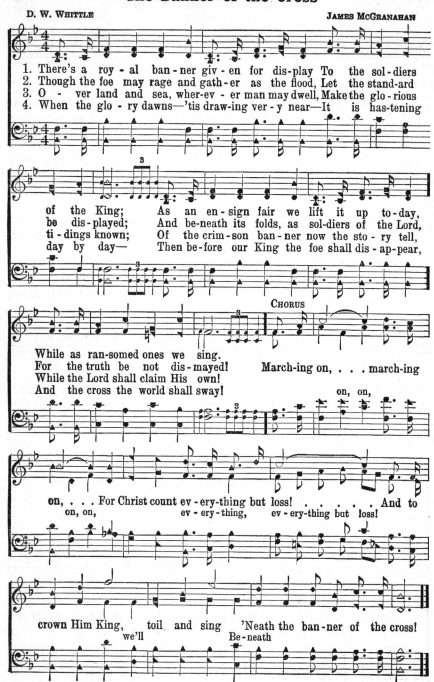

1. There's a roy-al ban-ner giv-en for dis-play To the sol-diers
2. Though the foe may rage and gath-er as the flood, Let the stand-ard
3. O - ver land and sea, wher-ev - er man may dwell, Make the glo - rious
4. When the glo - ry dawns—'tis draw-ing ver - y near—It is has-tening

of the King;   As an en-sign fair we lift it up to-day,
be dis-played;   And be-neath its folds, as sol-diers of the Lord,
ti - dings known; Of the crim-son ban - ner now the sto - ry tell,
day by day—   Then be-fore our King the foe shall dis-ap-pear,

CHORUS

While as ran-somed ones we sing.
For the truth be not dis-mayed!   March-ing on, . . . march-ing
While the Lord shall claim His own!
And the cross the world shall sway!   on, on,

on, . . . For Christ count ev - ery-thing but loss! . . . . . And to
on, on,   ev - ery-thing, ev - ery-thing but loss!

crown Him King,   toil and sing 'Neath the ban-ner of the cross!
       we'll   Be-neath

11 We're Marching to Zion

ISAAC WATTS

ROBERT LOWRY

Spirited

1. Come, we that love the Lord, And let our joys be known, Join
2. Let those re-fuse to sing Who nev-er knew our God; But
3. The hill of Zi-on yields A thou-sand sa-cred sweets Be-
4. Then let our songs a-bound, And ev-ery tear be dry; We're

in a song with sweet ac-cord, Join in a song with sweet ac-cord,
chil-dren of the heaven-ly King, But chil-dren of the heaven-ly King,
fore we reach the heaven-ly fields, Be-fore we reach the heaven-ly fields,
marching thro' Im-man-uel's ground, We're marching thro' Im-man-uel's ground,

And thus sur - round the throne, And thus sur-round the throne.
May speak their joys a-broad, May speak their joys a-broad.
Or walk the gold-en streets, Or walk the gold-en streets.
To fair-er worlds on high, To fair-er worlds on high.

(1) And thus sur-round the throne, And thus sur-round the throne.

CHORUS

We're march-ing to Zi-on, Beau-ti-ful, beau-ti-ful Zi-on; We're
We're march-ing on to Zi-on,

march-ing up-ward to Zi-on, The beau-ti-ful cit-y of God.
Zi-on, Zi-on,

Sweeter As the Years Go By

Mrs. C. H. M.

Mrs. C. H. MORRIS

1. Of Je - sus' love that sought me, When I was lost in sin; Of won-drous
2. He trod in old Ju - de - a Life's path-way long a - go; The peo - ple
3. 'Twas won-drous love which led Him For us to suf - fer loss— To bear with-

grace that brought me Back to His fold a - gain; Of heights and depths of
thronged a - bout Him, His sav - ing grace to know; He healed the bro - ken-
out a mur - mur, The an - guish of the cross; With saints re-deemed in

mer - cy, Far deep - er than the sea, And high - er than the heav - ens,
heart - ed, And caused the blind to see; And still His great heart yearn-eth
glo - ry, Let us our voic - es raise, Till heaven and earth re - ech - o

CHORUS

My theme shall ev - er be. Sweet-er as the years go by,.......
In love for e - ven me. Sweet - er as the years go by, 'Tis
With our Re-deem-er's praise.

Sweet-er as the years go by; Rich - er, full - er, deep - er,
Sweet - er as the years go by;

Copyright, 1940, by Mrs. W. R. Lunk, Renewal. Nazarene Publishing House, owner. Used by per.

Sweeter As the Years Go By

Je - sus' love is sweet - er, Sweet - er as the years go by.

13   Beautiful Redeemer

B. B. McK.   B. B. McKinney

1. Beau - ti - ful Re - deem - er, Lift me up to Thee;......
2. Beau - ti - ful Re - deem - er, Pure and just Thou art;........
3. Beau - ti - ful Re - deem - er, At Thy feet I fall.........

Let Thy love un - fail - ing Be re - vealed in me.
Reign su - preme for - ev - er In my yield - ed heart.
Let me serve Thee on - ly With my life, my all!

CHORUS

O my Sav - iour, bless me, Cleanse me, and con - fess me;

Mould me, and pos - sess me Ev - er as Thine own!

14 Faith Is the Victory

JOHN H. YATES

IRA D. SANKEY

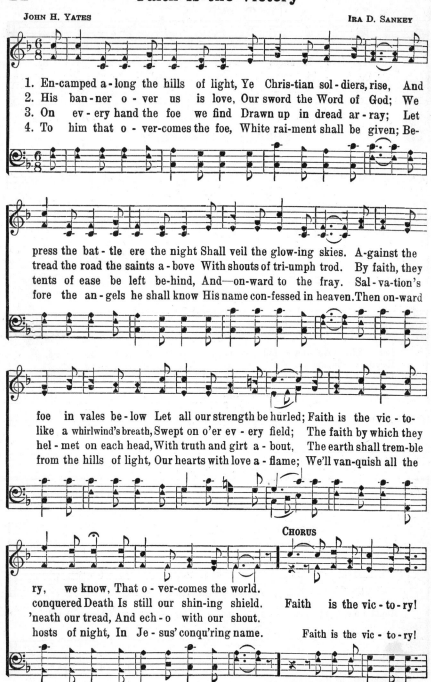

1. En-camped a-long the hills of light, Ye Chris-tian sol-diers, rise, And
2. His ban-ner o-ver us is love, Our sword the Word of God; We
3. On ev-ery hand the foe we find Drawn up in dread ar-ray; Let
4. To him that o-ver-comes the foe, White rai-ment shall be given; Be-

press the bat-tle ere the night Shall veil the glow-ing skies. A-gainst the
tread the road the saints a-bove With shouts of tri-umph trod. By faith, they
tents of ease be left be-hind, And—on-ward to the fray. Sal-va-tion's
fore the an-gels he shall know His name con-fessed in heaven.Then on-ward

foe in vales be-low Let all our strength be hurled; Faith is the vic-to-
like a whirlwind's breath, Swept on o'er ev-ery field; The faith by which they
hel-met on each head, With truth and girt a-bout, The earth shall trem-ble
from the hills of light, Our hearts with love a-flame; We'll van-quish all the

CHORUS

ry, we know, That o-ver-comes the world. Faith is the vic-to-ry!
conquered Death Is still our shin-ing shield.
'neath our tread, And ech-o with our shout.
hosts of night, In Je-sus' conqu'ring name. Faith is the vic-to-ry!

Faith Is the Victory

Faith is the vic-to-ry! Oh, glo-ri-ous vic-to-ry, That o-vercomes the world!
Faith is the vic-to-ry!

15   Take Time to Be Holy

W. D. LONGSTAFF   GEO. C. STEBBINS

1. Take time to be ho-ly, Speak oft with thy Lord; A-bide in Him
2. Take time to be ho-ly, The world rush-es on; Spend much time in
3. Take time to be ho-ly, Let Him be thy Guide, And run not be-
4. Take time to be ho-ly, Be calm in thy soul; Each tho't and each

al-ways, And feed on His Word. Make friends of God's chil-dren;
se-cret With Je-sus a-lone— By look-ing to Je-sus,
fore Him, What-ev-er be-tide; In joy or in sor-row,
mo-tive Be-neath His con-trol; Thus led by His Spir-it

Help those who are weak; For-get-ting in noth-ing His bless-ing to seek.
Like Him thou shalt be; Thy friends by thy con-duct His likeness shall see.
Still fol-low thy Lord, And, look-ing to Je-sus, Still trust in His Word.
To foun-tains of love, Thou soon shalt be fit-ted For serv-ice a-bove.

16 Anywhere with Jesus

JESSIE H. BROWN and Mrs. C. M. ALEXANDER

D. B. TOWNER

1. An - y-where with Je-sus I can safe-ly go; An - y-where He leads me in this world be - low; An - y-where with-out Him dear-est joys would fade; An - y-where with Je - sus I am not a - fraid.

2. An - y-where with Je-sus I am not a - lone; Oth - er friends may fail me, He is still my own; Tho' His hand may lead me o - ver drear - y ways, An - y-where with Je - sus is a house of praise.

3. An - y-where with Je-sus o - ver land and sea, Tell - ing souls in dark - ness of sal - va - tion free; Read - y as He sum-mons me to go or stay, An - y-where with Je - sus when He points the way.

4. An - y-where with Je-sus I can go to sleep, When the dark-'ning shad - ows round a - bout me creep; Know-ing I shall wak - en nev - er more to roam, An - y-where with Je - sus will be home, sweet home.

CHORUS

An - y - where! an - y - where! Fear I can - not know;

An - y - where with Je - sus I can safe - ly go.

17 Standing On the Promises

R. K. C.

R. KELSO CARTER

1. Stand-ing on the prom-is-es of Christ my King, Thro' e-ter-nal a-ges
2. Stand-ing on the prom-is-es that can-not fail, When the howling storms of
3. Stand-ing on the prom-is-es of Christ the Lord, Bound to Him e-ter-nal-
4. Stand-ing on the prom-is-es I can-not fall, Lis-tening ev-ery mo-ment

let His prais-es ring; Glo-ry in the high-est, I will shout and sing,
doubt and fear as-sail, By the liv-ing word of God I shall pre-vail,
ly by love's strong cord, O-ver-com-ing dai-ly with the Spir-it's sword,
to the Spir-it's call, Rest-ing in my Sav-iour, as my all in all,

CHORUS.

Stand-ing on the prom-is-es of God. Stand - ing, stand - ing,
Standing on the promises, standing on the promises,

Stand-ing on the prom-is-es of God my Sav-iour; Stand - ing,
Standing on the prom-is-es,

stand - - ing, I'm stand-ing on the prom-is-es of God.
stand-ing on the prom-is-es,

18 Throw Out the Life-Line

Edward S. Ufford

E. S. Ufford
Arr. by George C. Stebbins

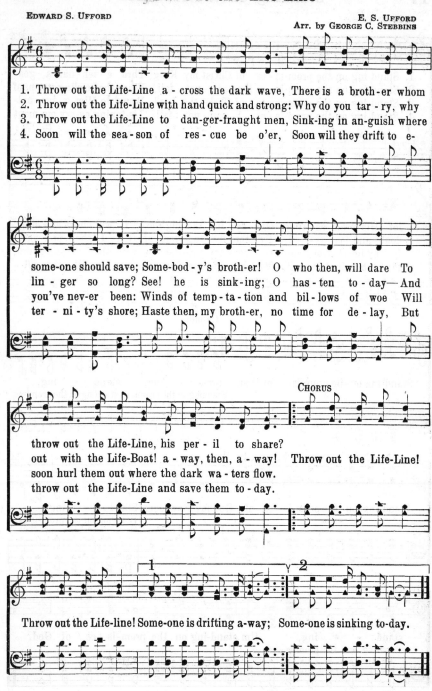

1. Throw out the Life-Line a - cross the dark wave, There is a broth-er whom some-one should save; Some-bod-y's broth-er! O who then, will dare To throw out the Life-Line, his per - il to share?

2. Throw out the Life-Line with hand quick and strong: Why do you tar - ry, why lin - ger so long? See! he is sink-ing; O has-ten to - day— And out with the Life-Boat! a - way, then, a - way!

3. Throw out the Life-Line to dan-ger-fraught men, Sink-ing in an-guish where you've nev-er been: Winds of temp - ta - tion and bil - lows of woe Will soon hurl them out where the dark wa - ters flow.

4. Soon will the sea - son of res - cue be o'er, Soon will they drift to e - ter - ni - ty's shore; Haste then, my broth-er, no time for de - lay, But throw out the Life-Line and save them to - day.

Chorus

Throw out the Life-Line! Throw out the Life-line! Some-one is drifting a-way; Some-one is sinking to-day.

Rescue the Perishing

FANNY J. CROSBY   WILLIAM H. DOANE

1. Res - cue the per-ish-ing, Care for the dy - ing, Snatch them in pit - y from
2. Tho' they are slighting Him, Still He is wait - ing, Wait-ing the pen - i - tent
3. Down in the hu-man heart, Crushed by the tempter, Feel-ings lie bur - ied that
4. Res - cue the per-ish-ing, Du - ty de-mands it; Strength for thy la-bor the

sin and the grave; Weep o'er the err - ing one, Lift up the fall - en,
child to re - ceive; Plead with them ear-nest-ly, Plead with them gen-tly,
grace can re - store; Touched by a lov - ing heart, Wak-ened by kind - ness,
Lord will pro-vide; Back to the nar-row way Pa - tient-ly win them;

CHORUS

Tell them of Je - sus the might - y to save.
He will for-give if they on - ly be - lieve. Res-cue the per - ish-ing,
Chords that are bro - ken will vi - brate once more.
Tell the poor wan-derer a Sav - iour has died.

Care for the dy - ing; Je - sus is mer - ci - ful, Je - sus will save.

I Am Resolved

Palmer Hartsough

J. H. Fillmore

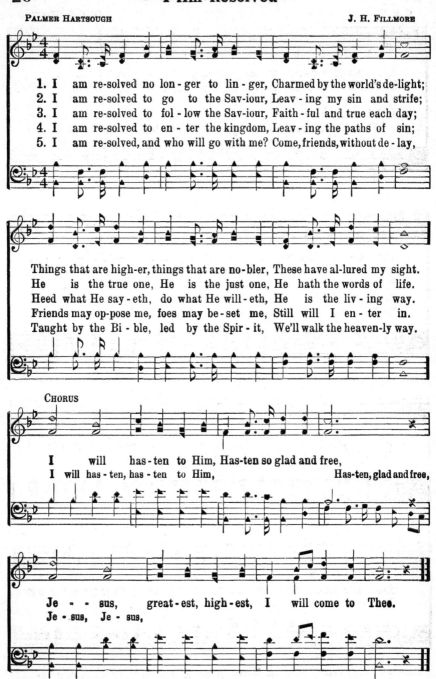

1. I am re-solved no lon-ger to lin-ger, Charmed by the world's de-light;
2. I am re-solved to go to the Sav-iour, Leav-ing my sin and strife;
3. I am re-solved to fol-low the Sav-iour, Faith-ful and true each day;
4. I am re-solved to en-ter the kingdom, Leav-ing the paths of sin;
5. I am re-solved, and who will go with me? Come, friends, without de-lay,

Things that are high-er, things that are no-bler, These have al-lured my sight.
He is the true one, He is the just one, He hath the words of life.
Heed what He say-eth, do what He will-eth, He is the liv-ing way.
Friends may op-pose me, foes may be-set me, Still will I en-ter in.
Taught by the Bi-ble, led by the Spir-it, We'll walk the heaven-ly way.

Chorus

I will has-ten to Him, Has-ten so glad and free,
I will has-ten, has-ten to Him, Has-ten, glad and free,

Je - - sus, great-est, high-est, I will come to Thee.
Je-sus, Je-sus,

21 My Saviour's Love

C. H. G.

CHAS. H. GABRIEL

1. I stand a-mazed in the pres-ence Of Je - sus the Naz - a - rene,
2. For me it was in the gar - den He prayed: "Not My will, but Thine;"
3. In pit - y an - gels be - held Him, And came from the world of light
4. He took my sins and my sor - rows, He made them His ver - y own;
5. When with the ransomed in glo - ry His face I at last shall see,

And won - der how He could love me, A sin-ner, condemned, un-clean.
He had no tears for His own griefs, But sweat-drops of blood for mine.
To com-fort Him in the sor - rows He bore for my soul that night.
He bore the bur - den to Cal - v'ry, And suf-fered, and died a - lone.
'Twill be my joy thro' the a - ges To sing of His love for me.

CHORUS.

How mar-vel-ous! how won-der-ful! And my song shall ev - er be:
Oh, how mar-vel-ous! oh, how won-der-ful!

How mar-vel-ous! how won-der-ful Is my Sav-ior's love for me! A-MEN.
Oh, how mar-vel-ous! oh, how won-der-ful

The Solid Rock

EDWARD MOTE

WILLIAM B. BRADBURY

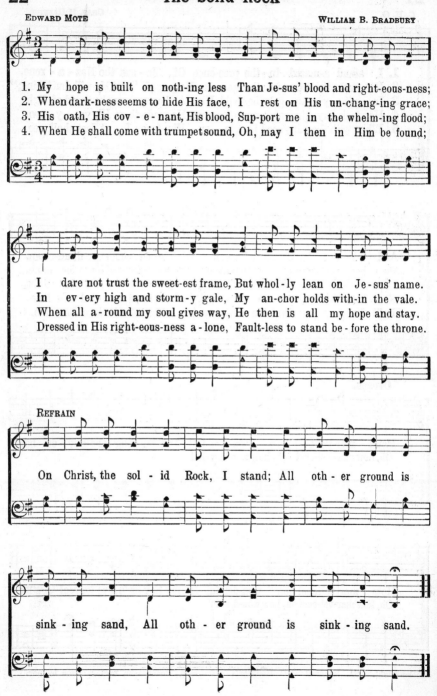

1. My hope is built on noth-ing less Than Je-sus' blood and right-eous-ness;
2. When dark-ness seems to hide His face, I rest on His un-chang-ing grace;
3. His oath, His cov - e - nant, His blood, Sup-port me in the whelm-ing flood;
4. When He shall come with trumpet sound, Oh, may I then in Him be found;

I dare not trust the sweet-est frame, But whol-ly lean on Je-sus' name.
In ev-ery high and storm-y gale, My an-chor holds with-in the vale.
When all a-round my soul gives way, He then is all my hope and stay.
Dressed in His right-eous-ness a-lone, Fault-less to stand be-fore the throne.

REFRAIN

On Christ, the sol - id Rock, I stand; All oth - er ground is

sink - ing sand, All oth - er ground is sink - ing sand.

23 There Shall Be Showers of Blessing

EL NATHAN

JAMES McGRANAHAN

1. "There shall be show-ers of bless-ing:" This is the prom-ise of love;
2. "There shall be show-ers of bless-ing"—Pre-cious re-viv-ing a-gain;
3. "There shall be show-ers of bless-ing:" Send them up-on us, O Lord;
4. "There shall be show-ers of bless-ing:" Oh, that to-day they might fall,

There shall be sea-sons re-fresh-ing, Sent from the Sav-iour a-bove.
O - ver the hills and the val-leys, Sound of a - bun-dance of rain.
Grant to us now a re-fresh-ing, Come, and now hon - or Thy Word.
Now as to God we're con-fess-ing, Now as on Je-sus we call!

CHORUS

Show - - ers of bless - ing, Show-ers of bless-ing we need:
Show - ers, show-ers of bless - ing,

Mer - cy-drops round us are fall - ing, But for the show-ers we plead.

24 Tell Me the Old, Old Story

KATE HANKEY

W. H. DOANE

1. Tell me the Old, Old Sto - ry, Of un-seen things a - bove, Of Je - sus
2. Tell me the sto - ry slow - ly, That I may take it in— That won-der-
3. Tell me the sto - ry soft - ly, With ear-nest tones and grave; Re - mem-ber
4. Tell me the same old sto - ry, When you have cause to fear Thatthisworld's

and His glo - ry, Of Je - sus and His love; Tell me the sto - ry
ful re - demp-tion, God's rem - e - dy for sin; Tell me the sto - ry
I'm the sin - ner Whom Je - sus came to save; Tell me the sto - ry
emp - ty glo - ry Is cost - ing me too dear; Yes, and when that world's

sim - ply, As to a lit - tle child, For I am weak and wea - ry,
of - ten, For I for - get so soon, The "ear - ly dew" of morn - ing
al - ways, If you would real - ly be, In an - y time of trou - ble,
glo - ry Is dawn - ing on my soul, Tell me the Old, Old Sto - ry:

CHORUS

And help - less and de - filed.
Has passed a - way at noon. Tell me the Old, Old Sto - ry, Tell me the
A com - fort - er to me.
"Christ Je - sus makes thee whole."

Old, Old Sto - ry, Tell me the Old, Old Sto - ry Of Je - sus and His love.

I Love to Tell the Story

CATHERINE HANKEY

WILLIAM G. FISCHER

1. I love to tell the sto - ry Of un - seen things a - bove, Of
2. I love to tell the sto - ry, More won - der - ful it seems Than
3. I love to tell the sto - ry, 'Tis pleas-ant to re - peat What
4. I love to tell the sto - ry, For those who know it best Seem

Je - sus and His glo - ry, Of Je - sus and His love. I love to
all the gold - en fan - cies Of all our gold - en dreams. I love to
seems, each time I tell it, More won - der - ful - ly sweet. I love to
hun - ger - ing and thirst-ing To hear it like the rest. And when, in

tell the sto - ry, Be - cause I know 'tis true; It sat - is - fies my
tell the sto - ry, It did so much for me; And that is just the
tell the sto - ry, For some have nev - er heard The mes - sage of sal -
scenes of glo - ry, I sing the new, new song, 'Twill be the old, old

CHORUS

long - ings As noth-ing else can do.
rea - son I tell it now to thee.   I love to tell the sto - ry, 'Twill
va - tion From God's own ho - ly Word.
sto - ry That I have loved so long.

be my theme in glo - ry To tell the old, old sto - ry Of Je-sus and His love.

26 The Shepherd of Love

A. S. R. .Albert Simpson Reitz.

1. The Shep-herd of Love is seek-ing the lost In paths that are rough and steep; He's call-ing the lambs that have gone a-stray, He's call-ing, call-ing His sheep.

2. The Shep-herd of Love knows His sheep by name, And ten-der-ly leads the way; O wea-ry one, come to the Shepherd's fold, He's call-ing, call-ing to-day.

3. The Shep-herd of Love our ran-som hath paid, And of-fers sal-va-tion free; He's pa-tient-ly wait-ing for thee to come, He's call-ing, call-ing for thee.

4. The Shep-herd of Love now seek-eth His sheep, He seek-eth what-e'er the cost; Be-hold, He is call-ing the wan-d'rer home, He's call-ing, call-ing the lost.

CHORUS.

Out of your dark-ness of sin and shame, In-to His love, for-ev-er the same; Come to Him now, be-lieve on His name, O an-swer the call to-day.

Call-ing, call-ing, Call-ing, call-ing,

Make Me a Channel of Blessing

H. G. S.

H. G. SMYTH

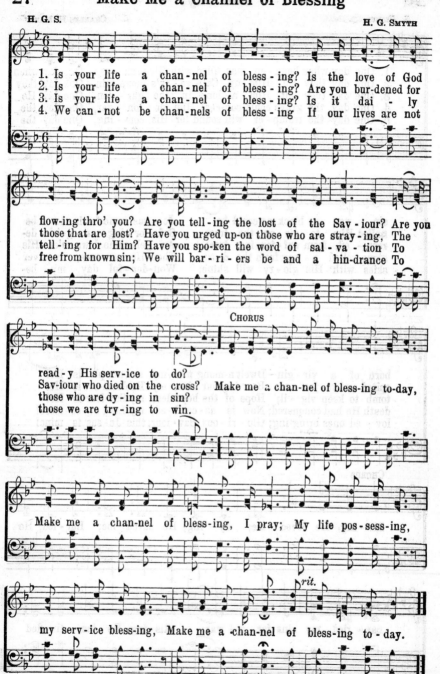

1. Is your life a chan-nel of bless-ing? Is the love of God
2. Is your life a chan-nel of bless-ing? Are you bur-dened for
3. Is your life a chan-nel of bless-ing? Is it dai - ly
4. We can-not be chan-nels of bless-ing If our lives are not

flow-ing thro' you? Are you tell-ing the lost of the Sav-iour? Are you
those that are lost? Have you urged up-on those who are stray-ing, The
tell - ing for Him? Have you spo-ken the word of sal-va - tion To
free from known sin; We will bar - ri - ers be and a hin-drance To

CHORUS

read - y His serv-ice to do? Make me a chan-nel of bless-ing to-day,
Sav-iour who died on the cross?
those who are dy - ing in sin?
those we are try-ing to win.

Make me a chan-nel of bless-ing, I pray; My life pos-sess-ing,

rit.

my serv-ice bless-ing, Make me a chan-nel of bless-ing to - day.

28 One Day!

J. WILBUR CHAPMAN   CHARLES H. MARSH

1. One day when heav-en was filled with His prais-es, One day when sin was as black as could be, Je-sus came forth to be born of a vir-gin—Dwelt a-mong men, my ex-am-ple is He!

2. One day they led Him up Cal-va-ry's moun-tain, One day they nailed Him to die on the tree; Suf-fer-ing an-guish, de-spised and re-ject-ed: Bear-ing our sins, my Re-deem-er is He!

3. One day they left Him a-lone in the gar-den, One day He rest-ed, from suf-fer-ing free; An-gels came down o'er His tomb to keep vig-il; Hope of the hope-less, my Sav-iour is He!

4. One day the grave could con-ceal Him no lon-ger, One day the stone rolled a-way from the door; Then He a-rose, o-ver death He had conquered; Now is as-cend-ed, my Lord ev-er-more!

5. One day the trump-et will sound for His com-ing, One day the skies with His glo-ry will shine; Won-der-ful day, my be-lov-ed ones bring-ing; Glo-ri-ous Sav-iour, this Je-sus is mine!

CHORUS

Liv-ing, He loved me; dy-ing, He saved me; Bur-ied, He car-ried my sins far a-way; Ris-ing, He jus-ti-fied

One Day!

free-ly for-ev-er: One day He's com-ing—oh, glo-ri-ous day!

29   I Know Whom I Have Believed

DANIEL W. WHITTLE (EL NATHAN)   JAMES McGRANAHAN

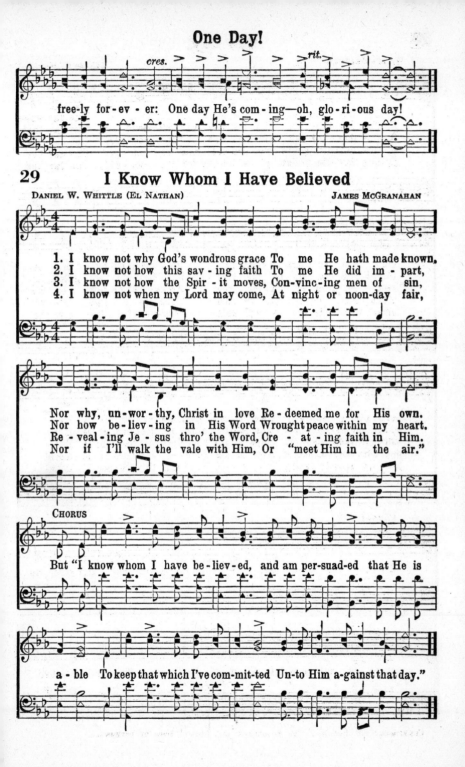

1. I know not why God's wondrous grace To me He hath made known,
2. I know not how this sav-ing faith To me He did im-part,
3. I know not how the Spir-it moves, Con-vinc-ing men of sin,
4. I know not when my Lord may come, At night or noon-day fair,

Nor why, un-wor-thy, Christ in love Re-deemed me for His own.
Nor how be-liev-ing in His Word Wrought peace within my heart.
Re-veal-ing Je-sus thro' the Word, Cre-at-ing faith in Him.
Nor if I'll walk the vale with Him, Or "meet Him in the air."

CHORUS

But "I know whom I have be-liev-ed, and am per-suad-ed that He is

a-ble To keep that which I've com-mit-ted Un-to Him a-gainst that day."

30 He Hideth My Soul

FANNY J. CROSBY

WM. J. KIRKPATRICK

Allegretto

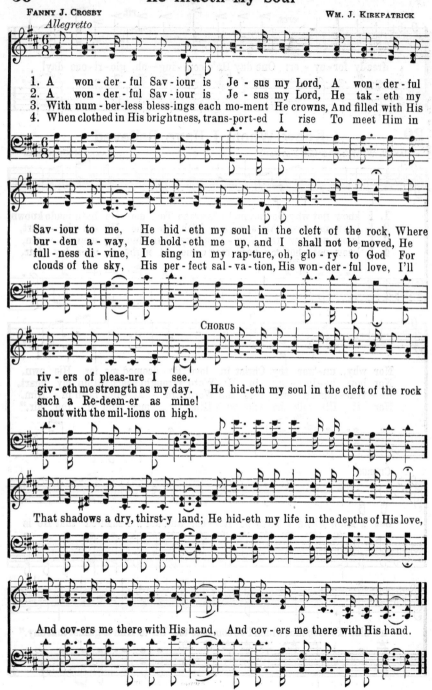

1. A won-der-ful Sav-iour is Je-sus my Lord, A won-der-ful
2. A won-der-ful Sav-iour is Je-sus my Lord, He tak-eth my
3. With num-ber-less bless-ings each mo-ment He crowns, And filled with His
4. When clothed in His brightness, trans-port-ed I rise To meet Him in

Sav-iour to me, He hid-eth my soul in the cleft of the rock, Where
bur-den a - way, He hold-eth me up, and I shall not be moved, He
full-ness di - vine, I sing in my rap-ture, oh, glo-ry to God For
clouds of the sky, His per-fect sal - va-tion, His won-der-ful love, I'll

riv-ers of pleas-ure I see.
giv-eth me strength as my day.
such a Re-deem-er as mine!
shout with the mil-lions on high.

CHORUS

He hid-eth my soul in the cleft of the rock

That shadows a dry, thirst-y land; He hid-eth my life in the depths of His love,

And cov-ers me there with His hand, And cov-ers me there with His hand.

31 He Included Me

REV. J. OATMAN, JR.　　　　　　　　　　　　　　　　HAMP SEWELL

1. I am so hap-py in Christ to-day, That I go sing-ing a-long my way;
2. Glad-ly I read, "Who-so-ev-er may Come to the fountain of life to-day;"
3. Ever God's Spirit is saying, "Come!" Hear the Bride saying, "No longer roam;"
4. "Freely come drink," words the soul to thrill! O with what joy they my heart do fill!

Yes, I'm so hap-py to know and say, "Je-sus in-clud-ed me too."
But when I read it I al-ways say, "Je-sus in-clud-ed me too."
But I am sure while they're calling home, Je-sus in-clud-ed me too.
For when He said, "Who-so-ev-er will," Je-sus in-clud-ed me too.

CHORUS.

Je-sus in-clud-ed me, Yes, He in-clud-ed me, When the Lord said "Who-so-ev-er," He in-clud-ed me; Je-sus in-clud-ed me, Yes, He in-clud-ed me, When the Lord said "Who-so-ev-er," He included me. A-MEN.

32 Hark, Hark, My Soul!

FREDERICK W. FABER VOX ANGELICA HENRY SMART

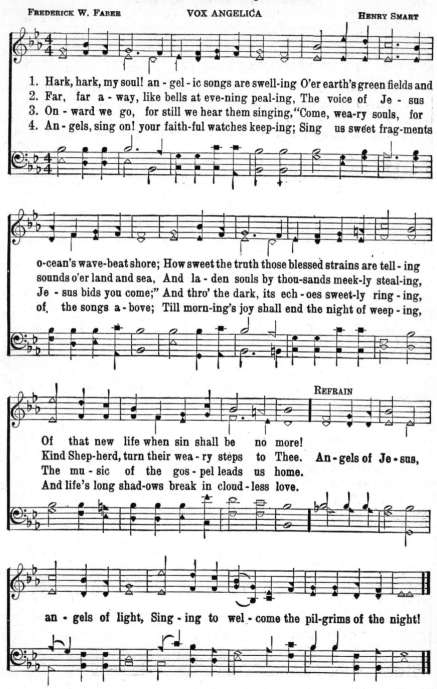

1. Hark, hark, my soul! an-gel-ic songs are swell-ing O'er earth's green fields and
2. Far, far a-way, like bells at eve-ning peal-ing, The voice of Je-sus
3. On-ward we go, for still we hear them singing, "Come, wea-ry souls, for
4. An-gels, sing on! your faith-ful watches keep-ing; Sing us sweet frag-ments

o-cean's wave-beat shore; How sweet the truth those blessed strains are tell-ing
sounds o'er land and sea, And la-den souls by thou-sands meek-ly steal-ing,
Je-sus bids you come;" And thro' the dark, its ech-oes sweet-ly ring-ing,
of the songs a-bove; Till morn-ing's joy shall end the night of weep-ing,

Of that new life when sin shall be no more!
Kind Shep-herd, turn their wea-ry steps to Thee. An-gels of Je-sus,
The mu-sic of the gos-pel leads us home.
And life's long shad-ows break in cloud-less love.

REFRAIN

an-gels of light, Sing-ing to wel-come the pil-grims of the night!

33 It Is Well with My Soul

H. G. SPAFFORD   P. P. BLISS

1. When peace, like a riv-er, at-tend-eth my way, When sor-rows like
2. Though Sa-tan should buf-fet, tho' tri-als should come, Let this blest as-
3. My sin— oh, the bliss of this glo-ri-ous tho't—My sin—not in
4. And, Lord, haste the day when the faith shall be sight, The clouds be rolled

sea - bil-lows roll; What-ev-er my lot, Thou hast taught me to say,
sur-ance con-trol, That Christ has re-gard-ed my help-less es-tate,
part, but the whole—Is nailed to the cross and I bear it no more,
back as a scroll, The trump shall re-sound and the Lord shall de-scend,

CHORUS

It is well, it is well with my soul.
And hath shed His own blood for my soul. It is well . . . . with my
Praise the Lord, praise the Lord, O my soul!
"E - ven so"— it is well with my soul. It is well

soul, ... It is well, it is well with my soul.
with my soul,

34 The Old Rugged Cross

Rev. G. B.

Rev. GEO. BENNARD

1. On a hill far a-way stood an old rug-ged cross, The em-blem of
2. Oh, that old rug-ged cross so de-spised by the world, Has a won-drous at-
3. In the old rug-ged cross, stained with blood so di-vine, A won-drous
4. To the old rug-ged cross I will ev-er be true, Its shame and re-

suf-fering and shame; And I love that old cross where the dear-est and best
trac-tion for me; For the dear Lamb of God left His glo-ry a-bove,
beau-ty I see; For 'twas on that old cross Je-sus suf-fered and died,
proach glad-ly bear; Then He'll call me some day to my home far a-way,

CHORUS

For a world of lost sin-ners was slain.
To bear it to dark Cal-va-ry.
To par-don and sanc-ti-fy me.
Where His glo-ry for-ev-er I'll share.

So I'll cher-ish the old rug-ged
cross, the

cross, . . . Till my tro-phies at last I lay down; I will cling to the
old rug-ged cross,

old rug-ged cross, . . . And ex-change it some day for a crown.
cross, the old rug-ged cross,

35 Wonderful, Wonderful Jesus

ANNIE B. RUSSELL   ERNEST O. SELLERS

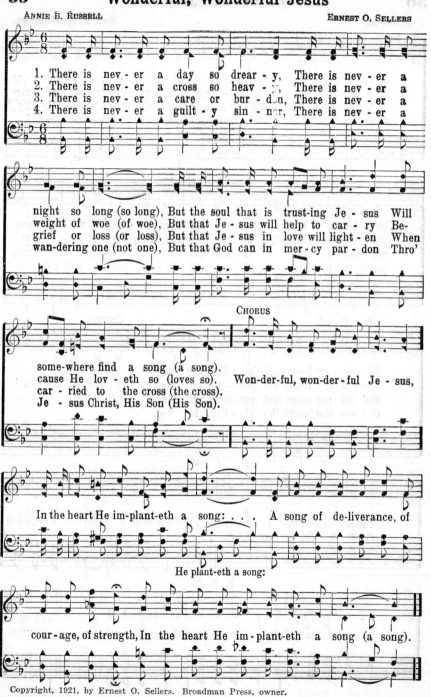

1. There is nev-er a day so drear-y, There is nev-er a
2. There is nev-er a cross so heav-y, There is nev-er a
3. There is nev-er a care or bur-den, There is nev-er a
4. There is nev-er a guilt-y sin-ner, There is nev-er a

night so long (so long), But the soul that is trust-ing Je-sus Will
weight of woe (of woe), But that Je-sus will help to car-ry Be-
grief or loss (or loss), But that Je-sus in love will light-en When
wan-dering one (not one), But that God can in mer-cy par-don Thro'

CHORUS

some-where find a song (a song).
cause He lov-eth so (loves so). Won-der-ful, won-der-ful Je-sus,
car-ried to the cross (the cross).
Je-sus Christ, His Son (His Son).

In the heart He im-plant-eth a song: ... A song of de-liverance, of

He plant-eth a song:

cour-age, of strength, In the heart He im-plant-eth a song (a song).

I Must Tell Jesus

E. A. H.

Rev. E. A. Hoffman.

1. I must tell Je-sus all of my tri-als; I can-not bear these
2. I must tell Je-sus all of my troub-les; He is a kind, com-
3. Tempted and tried I need a great Sav-ior, One who can help my
4. O how the world to e-vil al-lures me! O how my heart is

bur-dens a-lone; In my dis-tress He kind-ly will help me;
pas-sion-ate Friend; If I but ask Him, He will de-liv-er,
bur-dens to bear; I must tell Je-sus, I must tell Je-sus,
tempt-ed to sin! I must tell Je-sus, and He will help me

CHORUS.

He ev-er loves and cares for His own.
Make of my troub-les quick-ly an end. I must tell Je-sus!
He all my cares and sor-rows will share.
O-ver the world the vic-t'ry to win.

I must tell Je-sus! I can-not bear my bur-dens a-lone; I must tell

Je-sus! I must tell Je-sus! Je-sus can help me, Je-sus a-lone. A-MEN.

Will Jesus Find Us Watching?

FANNY J. CROSBY

W. H. DOANE

1. When Jesus comes to reward His servants, Whether it be
2. If, at the dawn of the early morning, He shall call us
3. Have we been true to the trust He left us? Do we seek to
4. Blessed are those whom the Lord finds watching, In His glory

noon or night, Faithful to Him will He find us watching,
one by one, When to the Lord we restore our talents,
do our best? If in our hearts there is naught condemns us,
they shall share; If He shall come at the dawn or midnight,

rit.

With our lamps all trimmed and bright?
Will He answer thee—Well done?
We shall have a glorious rest.
Will He find us watching there?

CHORUS

O can we say we are

ready, brother? Ready for the soul's bright home? Say, will He

find you and me still watching, Waiting, waiting when the Lord shall come?

38 Ye Must Be Born Again

W. T. SLEEPER

GEORGE C. STEBBINS

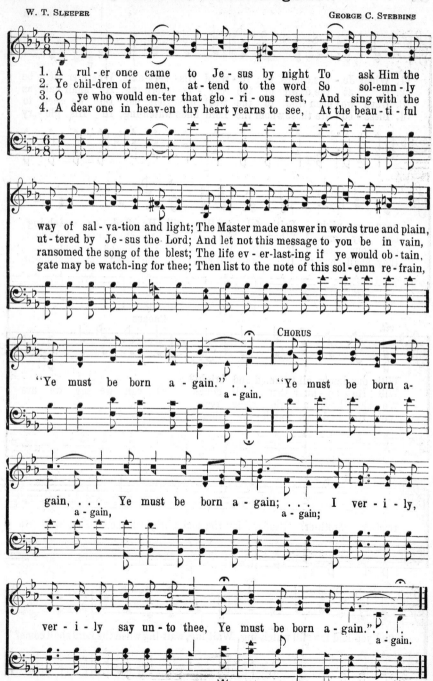

1. A rul-er once came to Je-sus by night To ask Him the
2. Ye chil-dren of men, at-tend to the word So sol-emn-ly
3. O ye who would en-ter that glo-ri-ous rest, And sing with the
4. A dear one in heav-en thy heart yearns to see, At the beau-ti-ful

way of sal-va-tion and light; The Master made answer in words true and plain,
ut-tered by Je-sus the Lord; And let not this message to you be in vain,
ransomed the song of the blest; The life ev-er-last-ing if ye would ob-tain,
gate may be watch-ing for thee; Then list to the note of this sol-emn re-frain,

CHORUS

"Ye must be born a-gain." . . "Ye must be born a-
a-gain.

gain, . . . Ye must be born a-gain; . . . I ver-i-ly,
a-gain,   a-gain;

ver-i-ly say un-to thee, Ye must be born a-gain." . .
a-gain.

The Nail-Scarred Hand

B. B. McK.

B. B. McKinney

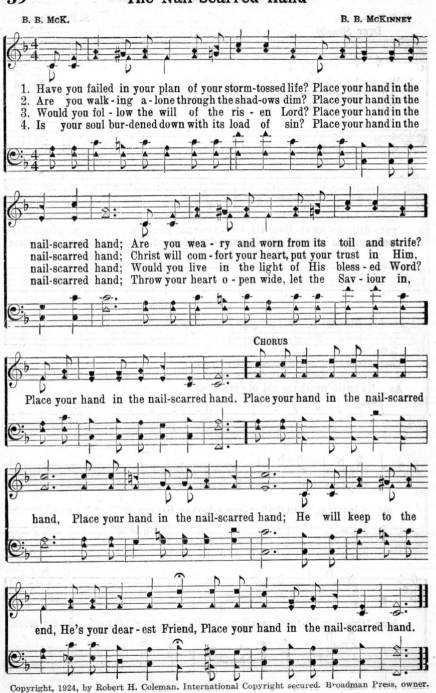

1. Have you failed in your plan of your storm-tossed life? Place your hand in the
2. Are you walk-ing a-lone through the shad-ows dim? Place your hand in the
3. Would you fol-low the will of the ris-en Lord? Place your hand in the
4. Is your soul bur-dened down with its load of sin? Place your hand in the

nail-scarred hand; Are you wea-ry and worn from its toil and strife?
nail-scarred hand; Christ will com-fort your heart, put your trust in Him,
nail-scarred hand; Would you live in the light of His bless-ed Word?
nail-scarred hand; Throw your heart o-pen wide, let the Sav-iour in,

CHORUS

Place your hand in the nail-scarred hand. Place your hand in the nail-scarred

hand, Place your hand in the nail-scarred hand; He will keep to the

end, He's your dear-est Friend, Place your hand in the nail-scarred hand.

40 'Neath the Old Olive Trees

B. B. McK. B. B. McKINNEY

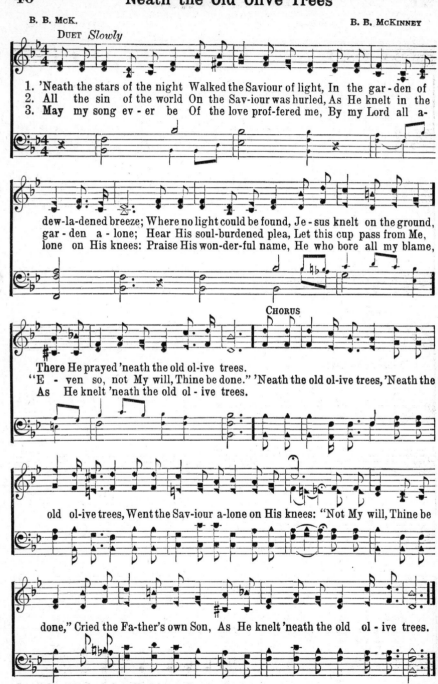

Duet *Slowly*

1. 'Neath the stars of the night Walked the Saviour of light, In the gar-den of
2. All the sin of the world On the Sav-iour was hurled, As He knelt in the
3. May my song ev-er be Of the love prof-fered me, By my Lord all a-

dew-la-dened breeze; Where no light could be found, Je-sus knelt on the ground,
gar-den a-lone; Hear His soul-burdened plea, Let this cup pass from Me,
lone on His knees: Praise His won-der-ful name, He who bore all my blame,

Chorus

There He prayed 'neath the old ol-ive trees.
"E - ven so, not My will, Thine be done." 'Neath the old ol-ive trees, 'Neath the
As He knelt 'neath the old ol - ive trees.

old ol-ive trees, Went the Sav-iour a-lone on His knees: "Not My will, Thine be

done," Cried the Fa-ther's own Son, As He knelt 'neath the old ol - ive trees.

41 Blessed Redeemer

AVIS BURGESON CHRISTIANSEN

HARRY DIXON LOES

1. Up Cal-vary's mountain one dreadful morn, Walked Christ my Saviour, weary and worn;
2. "Fa-ther, forgive them!" thus did He pray, E'en while His life-blood flowed fast a-way;
3. O how I love Him, Sav-iour and Friend, How can my prais-es ev-er find end!

Fac-ing for sin-ners death on the cross, That He might save them from endless loss.
Pray-ing for sin-ners while in such woe— No one but Je-sus ev-er loved so.
Thro' years un-num-bered on heaven's shore, My tongue shall praise Him for-ev-er-more.

CHORUS

Bless-ed Re-deem - er! pre-cious Re-deem - er! Seems now I
Bless-ed Re-deem-er! bless-ed Re-deem - er!

see Him on Cal-va-ry's tree; Wound-ed and bleed - ing, for sin-ners
Wound-ed and bleed-ing,

plead - ing— Blind and un-heed - - ing— dy-ing for me!
for sin-ners plead-ing— Blind and un-heed - ing—

42   Sweet Peace, the Gift of God's Love

P. P. B.

P. P. BILHORN

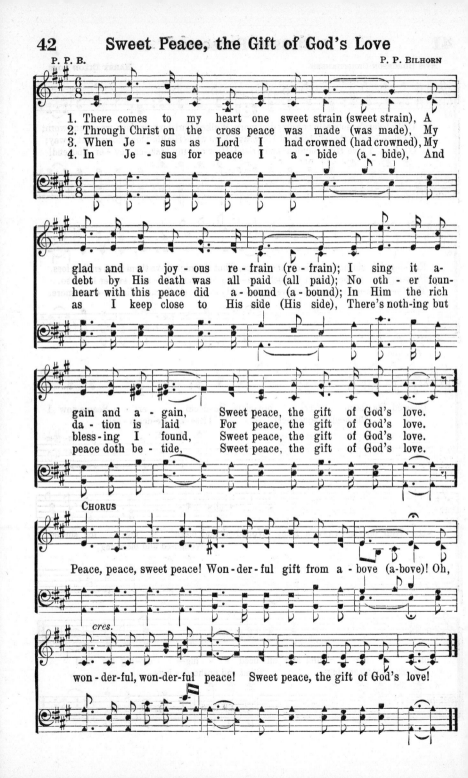

1. There comes to my heart one sweet strain (sweet strain), A
2. Through Christ on the cross peace was made (was made), My
3. When Je - sus as Lord I had crowned (had crowned), My
4. In Je - sus for peace I a - bide (a - bide), And

glad and a joy - ous re - frain (re - frain); I sing it a -
debt by His death was all paid (all paid); No oth - er foun -
heart with this peace did a - bound (a - bound); In Him the rich
as I keep close to His side (His side), There's noth-ing but

gain and a - gain,   Sweet peace, the gift of God's love.
da - tion is laid   For peace, the gift of God's love.
bless - ing I found,   Sweet peace, the gift of God's love.
peace doth be - tide,   Sweet peace, the gift of God's love.

CHORUS

Peace, peace, sweet peace! Won - der - ful gift from a - bove (a-bove)! Oh,

cres.

won - der-ful, won-der-ful peace! Sweet peace, the gift of God's love!

43 'Tis the Blessed Hour of Prayer

FANNY J. CROSBY

WILLIAM H. DOANE

1. 'Tis the bless-ed hour of prayer, when our hearts low-ly bend,
2. 'Tis the bless-ed hour of prayer, when the Sav-iour draws near,
3. 'Tis the bless-ed hour of prayer, when the tempt-ed and tried
4. At the bless-ed hour of prayer, trust-ing Him we be-lieve

And we gath-er to Je-sus, our Sav-iour and Friend; If we
With a ten-der com-pas-sion His chil-dren to hear; When He
To the Sav-iour who loves them their sor-row con-fide; With a
That the bless-ings we're need-ing we'll sure-ly re-ceive; In the

come to Him in faith, His pro-tec-tion to share, What a balm for the
tells us we may cast at His feet ev-ery care, What a balm for the
sym-pa-thiz-ing heart He re-moves ev-ery care; What a balm for the
full-ness of this trust we shall lose ev-ery care; What a balm for the

CHORUS

wea-ry! O how sweet to be there! Bless-ed hour of prayer, Bless-ed

hour of prayer; What a balm for the wea-ry! O how sweet to be there!

44 Saved, Saved!

J. P. S.

J. P. SCHOLFIELD

1. I've found a friend who is all to me, His
2. He saves me from ev-er-y sin and harm, Se-
3. When poor and need-y and all a-lone, In

love is ev-er true; . . . . . I love to tell how He
cures my soul each day; . . . . . I'm lean-ing strong on His
love He said to me, ... "Come un-to Me and I'll

lift-ed me And what His grace can do for you. . . .
might-y arm; I know He'll guide me all the way. . . .
lead you home, To live with Me e-ter-nal-ly." . . .

CHORUS

Saved . . . . by His power di-vine, Saved . . . . to new life sub-lime!
Saved by His power, Saved to new life,

cres. *rit.*

Life now is sweet and my joy is com-plete, For I'm saved, saved, saved!

45   The Lily of the Valley

English Melody

1. I have found a friend in Je-sus, He's ev-ery-thing to me, He's the
2. He all my griefs has tak-en, and all my sor-rows borne; In temp-
3. He will nev-er, nev-er leave me, nor yet for-sake me here, While I

fair-est of ten thou-sand to my soul; The Lil-y of the Val-ley,
ta-tion He's my strong and mighty tower; I have all for Him for-sak-en,
live by faith and do His bless-ed will; A wall of fire a-bout me,

D. S.—*Lil-y of the Val-ley,*

FINE.

in Him a-lone I see All I need to cleanse and make me ful-ly whole.
and all my i-dols torn From my heart, and now He keeps me by His power.
I've noth-ing now to fear, With His man-na He my hun-gry soul shall fill.

the Bright and Morn-ing Star, He's the fair-est of ten thou-sand to my soul.

In sor-row He's my com-fort, in trou-ble He's my stay,
Though all the world for-sake me, and Sa-tan tempt me sore,
Then sweep-ing up to glo-ry to see His bless-ed face,

D. S.

He tells me ev-ery care on Him to roll: He's the
Through Je-sus I shall safe-ly reach the goal: He's the
Where riv-ers of de-light shall ev-er roll: He's the

46 Why Should He Love Me So?

R. H.

Robert Harkness.

1. Love sent my Sav - ior to die in my stead, Why should He
2. Nails pierced His hands and His feet for my sin, Why should He
3. O how He ag - o - nized there in my place, Why should He

love me so? Meek - ly to Cal - va - ry's cross He was led,
love me so? He suf - fered sore my sal - va - tion to win,
love me so? Noth - ing with - hold - ing my sin to ef - face,

CHORUS

Why should He love me so? . . Why should He love me so? . .

Why should He love me so? . . . Why should my Sav - ior to
love me so?

Cal - va - ry go? Why should He love me so? . . . .
love me so?

His Love Won My Heart

J. P. S.

J. P. Scholfield.

1. I heard a sweet story, I know its true, It took a firm grip on my soul;
2. I yield-ed my-self to this Christ divine, For sin was a bur-den to me;
3. And now I am singing a-long my way, Where once I was burdened and sad;

It told of a Sav-ior who came to save, And make a bro-ken life whole.
He lift-ed that burden and gave me peace, And set my cap-tive soul free.
Now He is my Shepherd, my Friend and Guide, And keeps my heart ev-er glad.

CHORUS.

His love won my heart, . . . A love that will nev-er de - part; . . . .
yes, won my heart,
no, nev-er de-part;

1.
He took sin a - way, and came in to stay, His love won my heart.

2.
I want to be faith-ful, and loy-al and true To the love that won my heart.

48   He Lives

A. H. A.   Rev. A. H. ACKLEY

1. I serve a ris-en Sav-iour, He's in the world to-day; I know that He is
2. In all the world a-round me I see His lov-ing care, And tho' my heart grows
3. Re-joice, re-joice, O Christian, lift up your voice and sing E - ter - nal hal - le-

liv-ing, what-ev-er men may say; I see His hand of mer - cy, I
wea-ry I nev-er will de-spair; I know that He is lead-ing, thro'
lu - jahs to Je - sus Christ the King! The Hope of all who seek Him, the

hear His voice of cheer, And just the time I need Him He's al - ways near.
all the storm-y blast, The day of His ap-pear-ing will come at last.
Help of all who find, None oth-er is so lov-ing, so good and kind.

REFRAIN *Spirited*

He lives, He lives, Christ Je-sus lives to-day! He walks with me and
He lives, He lives,

talks with me a-long life's nar-row way. He lives, He lives, sal-
He lives, He lives,

He Lives

va-tion to im-part! You ask me how I know He lives? He lives within my heart.

49 Rejoice

B. B. McK.

B. B. McKinney

1. Re-joice, re-joice in Christ the Sav-iour, Who died that we might live a-gain;
2. Re-joice, re-joice in His sal-va-tion, He of-fers free to one and all;
3. Re-joice, re-joice in Him for-ev-er, Who guides us in the homeward way;

Re-joice, re-joice, for He is com-ing, And on the earth shall reign.
Let ev-ery tribe and ev-ery na-tion Be-fore His pres-ence fall.
Re-joice, for He will leave us nev-er, He's with us day by day.

CHORUS

Re-joice, (Re-joice,) re-joice, (re-joice,) To-geth-er let our prais-es ring; Re-

joice, re-joice, re-joice, In Christ the coming King.

Re-joice, re-joice.

50 "Whosoever" Meaneth Me

J. E. M.
J. EDWIN McCONNELL

1. I am hap-py to-day and the sun shines bright, The clouds have been
2. All my hopes have been raised, O His name be praised, His glo-ry has
3. O what won-der-ful love, O what grace di-vine, That Je-sus should

rolled a-way; For the Sav-ior said, Who-so-ev-er will May
filled my soul; I've been lift-ed up, and from sin set free, His
die for me; I was lost in sin, for the world I pined, But

CHORUS

come with Him to stay (to stay).
blood has made me whole (me whole). "Who-so-ev-er," sure-ly mean-eth me,
now I am set free (set free).

Sure-ly mean-eth me, O sure-ly mean-eth me; "Who-so-ev-er,"

sure-ly mean-eth me, "Who-so-ev-er," mean-eth me.
mean-eth me.

51 That Will Be Glory for Me

Arr. from JAMES McGRANAHAN
by B. B. McKINNEY

P. P. BLISS

1. I know not the hour when my Lord will come To take me a-way to His
2. I know not the song that the an-gels sing, I know not the sound of the
3. I know not the form of my man-sion fair, I know not the name that I

own dear home; But I know that His pres-ence will light-en the gloom, And
harp's glad ring; But I know there'll be prais-es to Je-sus our King, And
then shall bear; But I know that my Sav-iour will wel-come me there, And

CHORUS

that will be glo-ry for me. And that will be glo-ry for me, ...
that will be glo-ry for me. And that will be glo-ry, be glo-ry for me,
that will be glo-ry for me.

Oh, that will be glo-ry for me; . . . . When I stand in His
Oh, that will be glo-ry, be glo-ry for me;

rit.

pres-ence, and like Him shall be, Oh, that will be glo-ry for me.

52 Have Faith In God

B. B. McK.

B. B. McKinney

1. Have faith in God when your path-way is lone-ly, He sees and knows all the way you have trod; Nev-er a-lone are the least of His chil-dren; Have faith in God, have faith in God.

2. Have faith in God when your prayers are un-an-swered, Your ear-nest plea He will nev-er for-get; Wait on the Lord, trust His Word and be pa-tient; Have faith in God, He'll an-swer yet.

3. Have faith in God in your pain and your sor-row, His heart is touched with your grief and de-spair; Cast all your cares and your bur-dens up-on Him, And leave them there, oh, leave them there.

4. Have faith in God though all else fail a-bout you; Have faith in God, He pro-vides for His own; He can-not fail though all king-doms shall per-ish, He rules, He reigns up-on His throne.

Chorus

Have faith in God, He's on His throne; Have faith in God, He watcheth o'er His own;

rit.

He can-not fail, He must pre-vail; Have faith in God, have faith in God.

53 To the Work

Fanny J. Crosby

W. H. Doane

1. To the work! to the work! we are serv-ants of God, Let us fol-low the
path that our Mas-ter has trod; With the balm of His coun-sel our
strength to re-new, Let us do with our might what our hands find to do.

2. To the work! to the work! let the hun-gry be fed; To the foun-tain of
life let the wea-ry be led; In the cross and its ban-ner our
glo-ry shall be, While we her-ald the ti-dings, "Sal-va-tion is free!"

3. To the work! to the work! there is la-bor for all; For the king-dom of
dark-ness and er-ror shall fall; And the name of Je-ho-vah ex-
alt-ed shall be, In the loud swell-ing cho-rus, "Sal-va-tion is free!"

4. To the work! to the work! in the strength of the Lord, And a robe and a
crown shall our la-bor re-ward, When the home of the faith-ful our
dwell-ing shall be, And we shout with the ransomed, "Sal-va-tion is free!"

CHORUS

Toil-ing on, toil-ing on, Toil-ing on, toil-ing on;
Toil-ing on, toil-ing on, Toil-ing on, toil-ing on;
Let us hope, let us watch, And la-bor till the Mas-ter comes.
and trust, and pray,

54   I Won't Have to Cross Jordan Alone

THOMAS RAMSEY   CHAS. E. DURHAM

1. When I come to the riv-er at end-ing of day, When the last winds of
2. Of-ten-times I'm for-sak-en, and wea-ry and sad, When it seems that my
3. Tho' the bil-lows of sor-row and trouble may sweep, Christ the Sav-iour will

1. When the last

sor-row have blown; There'll be some-bod-y wait-ing to show me the way,
friends have all gone; There is one tho't that cheers me and makes my heart glad,
care for His own; Till the end of the jour-ney, my soul He will keep,
winds of sor-row have blown;

CHORUS

I won't have to cross Jor-dan a-lone. I won't have to cross Jor-dan a-
I won't have to across

lone. . . . Je-sus died for my sins to a-tone; When the
Jor-dan a-lone,

SOLO ad lib.   PARTS

dark-ness I see, He'll be waiting for me, I won't have to cross Jordan a-lone.
Hum   Hum

55 Love Lifted Me

JAMES ROWE

HOWARD E. SMITH

1. I was sink-ing deep in sin, Far from the peaceful shore, Ver-y deep-ly
2. All my heart to Him I give, Ev-er to Him I'll cling, In His bless-ed
3. Souls in dan-ger, look a-bove, Je-sus com-plete-ly saves; He will lift you

stained with-in, Sink-ing to rise no more; But the Mas-ter of the sea
pres-ence live, Ev-er His prais-es sing. Love so might-y and so true
by His love Out of the an-gry waves. He's the Mas-ter of the sea,

Heard my de-spair-ing cry, From the wa-ters lift-ed me, Now safe am I.
Mer-its my soul's best songs; Faith-ful, lov-ing serv-ice, too, To Him be-longs.
Bil-lows His will o-bey; He your Sav-iour wants to be—Be saved to-day.

CHORUS

Love lift-ed me! .... Love lift-ed me! .... When noth-ing
e - ven me!   e - ven me!

else could help, Love lift-ed me.   Love lift-ed me.

56 The Morning Light Is Breaking

S. F. SMITH   WEBB   G. J. WEBB

1. The morn-ing light is break-ing, The dark-ness dis-ap-pears;
2. See hea-then na-tions bend-ing Be-fore the God of love,
3. Blest riv-er of sal-va-tion, Pur-sue thine on-ward way;
4. Rich dews of grace come o'er us In man-y a gen-tle shower,

The sons of earth are wak-ing To pen-i-ten-tial tears;
And thou-sand hearts as-cend-ing In grat-i-tude a-bove;
Flow thou to ev-ery na-tion, Nor in thy rich-ness stay;
And bright-er scenes be-fore us Are ope-ning ev-ery hour;

Each breeze that sweeps the o-cean Brings ti-dings from a-far,
While sin-ners, now con-fess-ing, The Gos-pel's call o-bey,
Stay not till all the low-ly Tri-um-phant reach their home;
Each cry to heav-en go-ing, A-bun-dant an-swer brings,

Of na-tions in com-mo-tion, Pre-pared for Zi-on's war.
And seek a Sav-iour's bless-ing, A na-tion in a day.
Stay not till all the ho-ly Pro-claim,"The Lord is come!"
And heaven-ly gales are blow-ing, With peace up-on their wings.

57 Saviour, Like a Shepherd Lead Us

DOROTHY A. THRUPP   SHEPHERD   WILLIAM B. BRADBURY

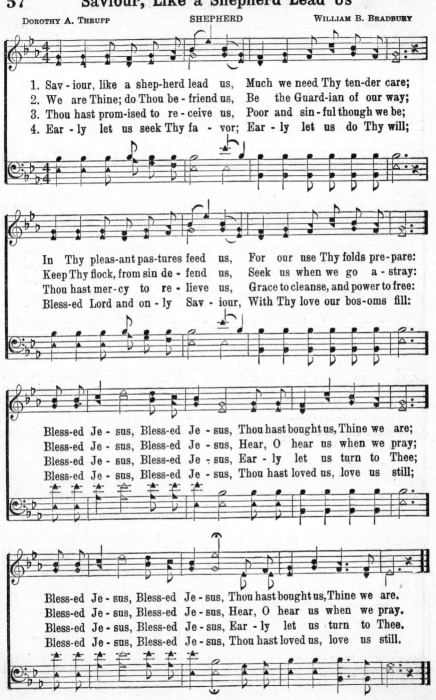

1. Sav - iour, like a shep-herd lead us, Much we need Thy ten-der care;
2. We are Thine; do Thou be - friend us, Be the Guard-ian of our way;
3. Thou hast prom-ised to re - ceive us, Poor and sin - ful though we be;
4. Ear - ly let us seek Thy fa - vor; Ear - ly let us do Thy will;

In Thy pleas-ant pas-tures feed us, For our use Thy folds pre-pare:
Keep Thy flock, from sin de - fend us, Seek us when we go a - stray:
Thou hast mer-cy to re - lieve us, Grace to cleanse, and power to free:
Bless-ed Lord and on - ly Sav - iour, With Thy love our bos-oms fill:

Bless-ed Je - sus, Bless-ed Je - sus, Thou hast bought us, Thine we are;
Bless-ed Je - sus, Bless-ed Je - sus, Hear, O hear us when we pray;
Bless-ed Je - sus, Bless-ed Je - sus, Ear - ly let us turn to Thee;
Bless-ed Je - sus, Bless-ed Je - sus, Thou hast loved us, love us still;

Bless-ed Je - sus, Bless-ed Je - sus, Thou hast bought us, Thine we are.
Bless-ed Je - sus, Bless-ed Je - sus, Hear, O hear us when we pray.
Bless-ed Je - sus, Bless-ed Je - sus, Ear - ly let us turn to Thee.
Bless-ed Je - sus, Bless-ed Je - sus, Thou hast loved us, love us still.

58 Prayer Changes Things

B. B. McK.   B. B. McKinney.

1. When the dark shad-ows come o - ver you, Bring-ing troubles you nev - er knew,
2. Prayer will bring peace when the days are long, Turn your sighing in - to a song,
3. Pray for the wan-der - er at your door, Pray for lost ones the wide world o'er;
4. Pray and take courage thro' weal or woe, In life's bat-tles on earth be - low;

Trust in the Sav-ior and pray it thro', For prayer chang-es things.
It will bring vic-to-ry o - ver wrong, For prayer chang-es things.
Je - sus will save them for-ev - er-more, For prayer chang-es things.
Pray with a faith that will not let go, For prayer chang-es things.

CHORUS

Prayer chang - es things, . . . Prayer chang - es things, ...
chang - es things,   chang - es things,

When the world is cold and blue, Trust in Je - sus, pray it through,

Vic - to - ry will come to you, For prayer chang - es things.

59   His Grace Is Sufficient for Me

W. W. Hamilton

B. B. McKinney.

1. When sin-stricken, burdened and wea-ry, From bondage I longed to be free,
2. Tho' tempt-ed and sad-ly dis-cour-aged, My soul to this ref-uge will flee,
3. My bark may be tossed by the tem-pest That sweeps o'er the tur-bu-lent sea;
4. When life here on earth is all o-ver, When Je-sus, my Sav-ior, I see,

There came to my heart the sweet message, "My grace is suf-fi-cient for thee."
And rest in the bless-ed as-sur-ance, "My grace is suf-fi-cient for thee."
A rain-bow il-lu-mines the dark-ness, "My grace is suf-fi-cient for thee."
I'll know as I dwell in His pres-ence, "His grace is suf-fi-cient for me."

CHORUS

His grace is suf-fi-cient for me, ... His grace is suf-
His grace is suf-fi-cient, suf-fi-cient for me, His grace is suf-

fi-cient for me; . . . . . In shad-y green pas-tures or
fi-cient, suf-fi-cient for me;

on the rough sea, His grace is suf-fi-cient for me.

Let the Tide Come In

Rev. David Ross.   B. B. McKinney.

1. We thank Thee, Lord, that pow'r is flowing, Joy is com-ing, sor-row go-ing;
2. Oh, let Thy cross win ev-'ry na-tion, Send the peo-ple Thy sal-va-tion!
3. Life's precious hours are quickly fly-ing, Men are dy-ing, ev-er dy-ing!
4. We praise Thee for the ti-dings cheer-ing, Signs of conquest now ap-pear-ing,

Thy ran-somed host is grow-ing, grow-ing, But may the tide come in.
A-mong them show Thy new cre-a-tion, Oh, may the tide come in.
Thy pleading Church is cry-ing, cry-ing, Now may the tide come in.
Thy day of vic-to-ry is near-ing, Thank God! the tide comes in.

CHORUS.

Let the tide come in, Let the tide come in, Let the cleans-ing

bil-lows sweep a-way our sin; Let the tide come in,

rit.

Let the tide come in, Oh, let the might-y tide come in.

Jesus Is Calling

FANNY J. CROSBY

GEO. C. STEBBINS

1. Je - sus is ten - der - ly call - ing thee home— Call - ing to - day,
2. Je - sus is call - ing the wea - ry to rest— Call - ing to - day,
3. Je - sus is wait - ing; O come to Him now— Wait - ing to - day,
4. Je - sus is plead - ing; O list to His voice: Hear Him to - day,

call - ing to - day; Why from the sun - shine of love wilt thou roam
call - ing to - day; Bring Him thy bur - den and thou shalt be blest;
wait - ing to - day; Come with thy sins; at His feet low - ly bow;
hear Him to - day; They who be - lieve on His name shall re - joice;

REFRAIN

Far-ther and far-ther a - way?
He will not turn thee a - way.
Come, and no lon - ger de - lay.
Quick-ly a - rise and a - way.

Call - - ing to - day, ...
Call - ing, call-ing to - day, to - day,

Call - - ing to - day, ...
Call - ing, call - ing to - day, to - day;

Je - - - sus is
Je - sus is ten - der - ly

call - - - - ing, Is ten - der - ly call - ing to - day.
call - ing to - day,

My Desire

J. P. S.

J. P. Scholfield

Spirited

1. I want my life to glo-ri-fy my Lord and King;   I want to please and
2. Oh, that my life might mag-ni-fy the Sav-ior's pow'r; Oh, that my deeds might
3. I want my life to tes-ti-fy that He can save;   I want to help to

hon-or Him in ev-'ry-thing; I want my life to tell men that He is   my
wit-ness to His grace each hour; Oh, that my words might magnify His ho-ly
make His crimson ban-ner wave; I want to tell the bless-ed sto-ry   ev-'ry

Chorus

Guide; I want the world to know He's walking by my side.
name, So let my heart and voice His mighty pow'r proclaim.   I want to live as
day;   I want to be a light to oth-ers on their way.

Je-sus lived, I want to love as Je-sus loved, I want to serve and honor Him and

please Him in ev-'ry-thing;   I want my life to tes-ti-fy that He's my Lord and King.

Able, Willing, Mighty

J. P. S.

J. P. SCHOLFIELD

1. Je-sus is a-ble to save from sin, Will you re-ceive Him to-day?
2. Je-sus is will-ing to save your soul, Will you re-ceive Him to-day?
3. Je-sus is might-y to hold you fast, Why not ac-cept Him to-day?

A-ble to plant the new life with-in, Will you re-ceive Him to-day?
Will-ing to take you and make you whole, Je-sus is will-ing to-day.
Might-y to keep you un-to the last; Je-sus is might-y to save.

CHORUS Unison   Parts   Unison

A-ble, a-ble, Jesus is a-ble to save; ... Will-ing, will-ing,
Je-sus is a-ble to save;

Parts   Unison   Parts

Je-sus is will-ing to save; .... Might-y, might-y, Je-sus is might-y to
Je-sus is will-ing to save; Je-sus is

save; .... Might-y, He's might-y, Je-sus is might-y to save.
might-y to save; yes, Je-sus is might-y,

Christ the Lord Is Risen Today

CHARLES WESLEY   WORGAN   From "Lyra Davidica"

1. Christ the Lord is risen to - day, Al - - - le - lu - ia!
2. Lives a - gain our glo - rious King: Al - - - le - lu - ia!
3. Love's re - deem-ing work is done, Al - - - le - lu - ia!
4. Soar we now, where Christ has led, Al - - - le - lu - ia!

Sons of men and an - gels say: Al - - - le - lu - ia!
Where, O death, is now thy sting? Al - - - le - lu - ia!
Fought the fight, the bat - tle won; Al - - - le - lu - ia!
Fol - lowing our ex - alt - ed Head; Al - - - le - lu - ia!

Raise your joys and tri - umphs high, Al - - - le - lu - ia!
Dy - ing once, He all doth save: Al - - - le - lu - ia!
Death in vain for - bids Him rise; Al - - - le - lu - ia!
Made like Him, like Him we rise; Al - - - le - lu - ia!

Sing, ye heavens, and earth, re - ply, Al - - - le - lu - ia!
Where thy vic - to - ry, O grave? Al - - - le - lu - ia!
Christ has o - pened Par - a - dise. Al - - - le - lu - ia!
Ours the cross, the grave, the skies. Al - - - le - lu - ia!

The Son of God Goes Forth to War

REGINALD HEBER   ALL SAINTS NEW   HENRY S. CUTLER

1. The Son of God goes forth to war, A king-ly crown to gain;
2. The mar-tyr first, whose ea-gle eye Could pierce be-yond the grave,
3. A glo-rious band, the cho-sen few On whom the Spir-it came,
4. A no-ble ar-my, men and boys, The ma-tron and the maid,

His blood-red ban-ner streams a-far: Who fol-lows in His train?
Who saw his Mas-ter in the sky, And called on Him to save:
Twelve valiant saints, their hope they knew, And mocked the cross and flame:
A-round the Sav-iour's throne re-joice, In robes of light ar-rayed:

Who best can drink his cup of woe, Tri-um-phant o-ver pain,
Like Him, with par-don on His tongue In midst of mor-tal pain,
They met the ty-rant's brandished steel, The li-on's go-ry mane;
They climbed the steep as-cent of heaven Thro' per-il, toil, and pain:

Who pa-tient bears his cross be-low, He fol-lows in His train.
He prayed for them that did the wrong: Who fol-lows in his train?
They bowed their necks the death to feel: Who fol-lows in their train?
O God, to us may grace be given To fol-low in their train.

66 The Church's One Foundation

Samuel J. Stone

Samuel S. Wesley

1. The Church-'s one foun-da - tion Is Je - sus Christ her Lord;
2. E - lect from ev - ery na - tion, Yet one o'er all the earth,
3. 'Mid toil and trib - u - la - tion, And tu - mult of her war,
4. Yet she on earth hath un - ion With God the Three in One,

She is His new cre - a - tion By Spir - it and the Word:
Her char - ter of sal - va - tion, One Lord, one faith, one birth;
She waits the con - sum - ma - tion Of peace for - ev - er - more;
And mys - tic sweet com - mun - ion With those whose rest is won:

From heaven He came and sought her To be His ho - ly bride;
One ho - ly name she bless - es, Par - takes one ho - ly food,
Till, with the vi - sion glo - rious, Her long - ing eyes are blest,
O hap - py ones and ho - ly! Lord, give us grace that we,

With His own blood He bought her, And for her life He died.
And to one hope she press - es, With ev - ery grace en - dued.
And the great Church vic - to - rious Shall be the Church at rest.
Like them, the meek and low - ly, On high may dwell with Thee.

The Lord Is My Shepherd

JAMES MONTGOMERY

THOMAS KOSCHAT

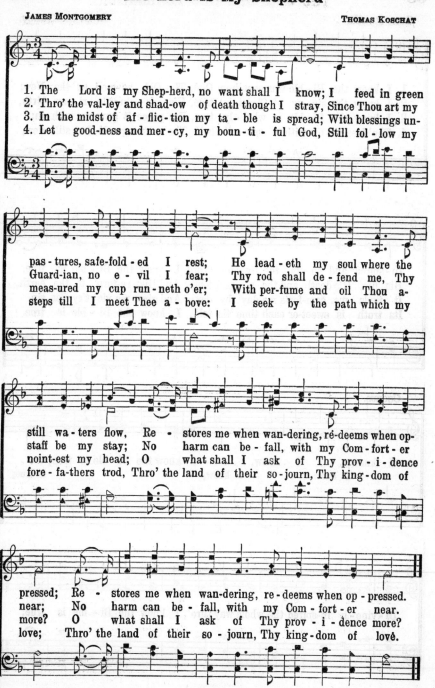

1. The Lord is my Shep-herd, no want shall I know; I feed in green pas-tures, safe-fold-ed I rest; He lead-eth my soul where the still wa-ters flow, Re - stores me when wan-dering, ré-deems when op-pressed; Re - stores me when wan-dering, re-deems when op-pressed.

2. Thro' the val-ley and shad-ow of death though I stray, Since Thou art my Guard-ian, no e-vil I fear; Thy rod shall de-fend me, Thy staff be my stay; No harm can be-fall, with my Com-fort-er near; No harm can be-fall, with my Com-fort-er near.

3. In the midst of af-flic-tion my ta-ble is spread; With blessings un-meas-ured my cup run-neth o'er; With per-fume and oil Thou a-noint-est my head; O what shall I ask of Thy prov-i-dence more? O what shall I ask of Thy prov-i-dence more?

4. Let good-ness and mer-cy, my boun-ti-ful God, Still fol-low my steps till I meet Thee a-bove: I seek by the path which my fore-fa-thers trod, Thro' the land of their so-journ, Thy king-dom of love; Thro' the land of their so-journ, Thy king-dom of love.

68 I Know the Bible Is True

Gene Routh.

B. B. McKinney.

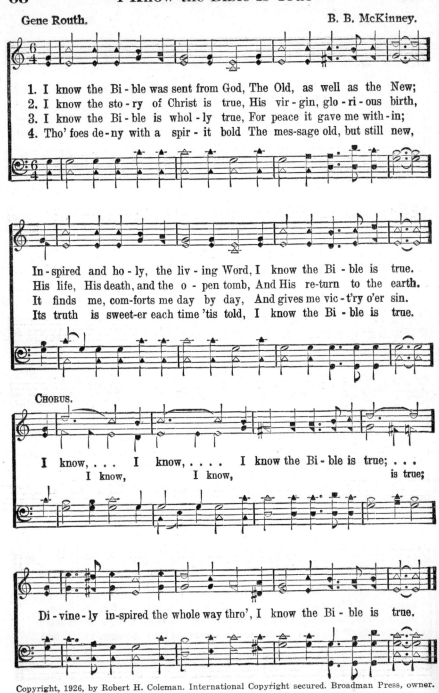

1. I know the Bi - ble was sent from God, The Old, as well as the New;
2. I know the sto - ry of Christ is true, His vir - gin, glo - ri - ous birth,
3. I know the Bi - ble is whol - ly true, For peace it gave me with - in;
4. Tho' foes de - ny with a spir - it bold The mes-sage old, but still new,

In - spired and ho - ly, the liv - ing Word, I know the Bi - ble is true.
His life, His death, and the o - pen tomb, And His re-turn to the earth.
It finds me, com-forts me day by day, And gives me vic - t'ry o'er sin.
Its truth is sweet-er each time 'tis told, I know the Bi - ble is true.

CHORUS.

I know, ... I know, ... I know the Bi - ble is true; ...
I know, I know, is true;

Di - vine - ly in-spired the whole way thro', I know the Bi - ble is true.

Jesus, I Come

W. T. Sleeper

Geo. C. Stebbins

1. Out of my bond-age, sor-row and night, Je-sus, I come, Je-sus, I come;
2. Out of my shame-ful fail-ure and loss, Je-sus, I come, Je-sus, I come;
3. Out of un-rest and ar-ro-gant pride, Je-sus, I come, Je-sus, I come;
4. Out of the fear and dread of the tomb, Je-sus, I come, Je-sus, I come;

In - to Thy free-dom, glad-ness and light, Je-sus, I come to Thee;
In - to the glo-rious gain of Thy cross, Je-sus, I come to Thee;
In - to Thy bless-ed will to a - bide, Je-sus, I come to Thee;
In - to the joy and light of Thy home, Je-sus, I come to Thee;

Out of my sick-ness in-to Thy health, Out of my want and in-to Thy wealth,
Out of earth's sorrows in-to Thy balm, Out of life's storms and in-to Thy calm,
Out of my-self to dwell in Thy love, Out of de-spair in-to rap-tures a-bove,
Out of the depths of ru - in un - told, In - to the peace of Thy sheltering fold,

Out of my sin and in - to Thy-self, Je-sus, I come to Thee.
Out of dis-tress to ju - bi-lant psalm, Je-sus, I come to Thee.
Up-ward for aye on wings like a dove, Je-sus, I come to Thee.
Ev - er Thy glo-rious face to be-hold, Je-sus, I come to Thee.

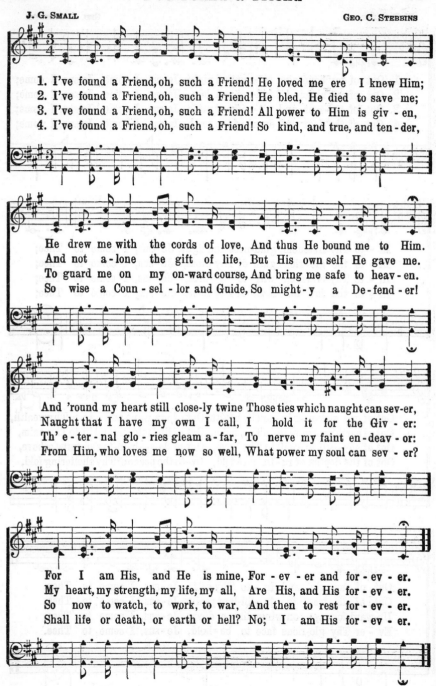

70 I've Found a Friend

J. G. SMALL

GEO. C. STEBBINS

1. I've found a Friend, oh, such a Friend! He loved me ere I knew Him;
2. I've found a Friend, oh, such a Friend! He bled, He died to save me;
3. I've found a Friend, oh, such a Friend! All power to Him is giv-en,
4. I've found a Friend, oh, such a Friend! So kind, and true, and ten-der,

He drew me with the cords of love, And thus He bound me to Him.
And not a-lone the gift of life, But His own self He gave me.
To guard me on my on-ward course, And bring me safe to heav-en.
So wise a Coun-sel-lor and Guide, So might-y a De-fend-er!

And 'round my heart still close-ly twine Those ties which naught can sev-er,
Naught that I have my own I call, I hold it for the Giv-er:
Th' e-ter-nal glo-ries gleam a-far, To nerve my faint en-deav-or:
From Him, who loves me now so well, What power my soul can sev-er?

For I am His, and He is mine, For-ev-er and for-ev-er.
My heart, my strength, my life, my all, Are His, and His for-ev-er.
So now to watch, to work, to war, And then to rest for-ev-er.
Shall life or death, or earth or hell? No; I am His for-ev-er.

71 Let Him In

J. B. Atchinson

E. O. Excell

1. There's a Stran-ger at the door, Let Him in;
2. O - pen now to Him your heart, Let Him in;
3. Hear you now His lov-ing voice? Let Him in;
4. Now ad-mit the heaven-ly Guest, Let Him in;

Let the Sav-iour in, Let the Sav-iour in;

He has been there oft be-fore, Let Him in;
If you wait He will de-part, Let Him in;
Now, oh, now make Him your choice, Let Him in;
He will make for you a feast, Let Him in;

Let the Sav-iour in, Let the Sav-iour in;

Let Him in, ere He is gone, Let Him in, the Ho-ly One,
Let Him in, He is your Friend, He your soul will sure de-fend,
He is stand-ing at your door, Joy to you He will re-store,
He will speak your sins for-given, And when earth ties all are riven,

Je - sus Christ, the Fa-ther's Son, Let Him in.
He will keep you to the end, Let Him in.
And His name you will a - dore, Let Him in.
He will take you home to heaven, Let Him in.

Let the Sav-iour in, Let the Sav-iour in.

72 Jesus, I My Cross Have Taken

HENRY F. LYTE   ELLESDIE   From MOZART

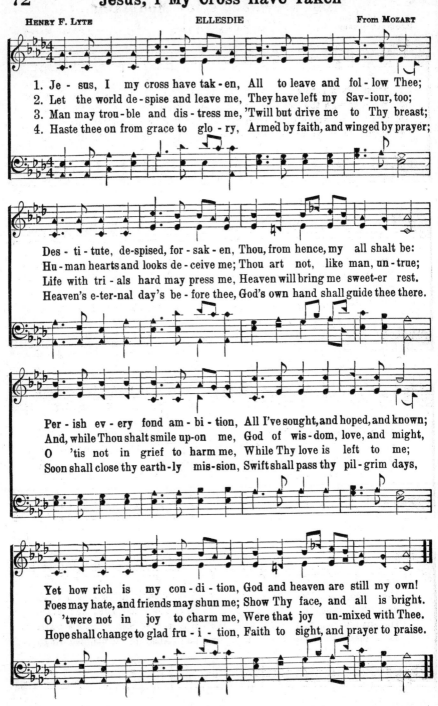

1. Je - sus, I my cross have tak - en, All to leave and fol - low Thee;
2. Let the world de - spise and leave me, They have left my Sav - iour, too;
3. Man may trou - ble and dis - tress me, 'Twill but drive me to Thy breast;
4. Haste thee on from grace to glo - ry, Armed by faith, and winged by prayer;

Des - ti - tute, de - spised, for - sak - en, Thou, from hence, my all shalt be:
Hu - man hearts and looks de - ceive me; Thou art not, like man, un - true;
Life with tri - als hard may press me, Heaven will bring me sweet - er rest.
Heaven's e - ter - nal day's be - fore thee, God's own hand shall guide thee there.

Per - ish ev - ery fond am - bi - tion, All I've sought, and hoped, and known;
And, while Thou shalt smile up - on me, God of wis - dom, love, and might,
O 'tis not in grief to harm me, While Thy love is left to me;
Soon shall close thy earth - ly mis - sion, Swift shall pass thy pil - grim days,

Yet how rich is my con - di - tion, God and heaven are still my own!
Foes may hate, and friends may shun me; Show Thy face, and all is bright.
O 'twere not in joy to charm me, Were that joy un - mixed with Thee.
Hope shall change to glad fru - i - tion, Faith to sight, and prayer to praise.

From Greenland's Icy Mountains

REGINALD HEBER   MISSIONARY HYMN   LOWELL MASON

1. From Green-land's i - cy moun-tains, From In - dia's cor - al strand;
2. What though the spi - cy breez - es Blow soft o'er Cey-lon's isle;
3. Shall we, whose souls are light - ed With wis-dom from on high,
4. Waft, waft, ye winds, His sto - ry, And you, ye wa-ters, roll,

Where Af - ric's sun - ny foun - tains Roll down their gold - en sand:
Though ev - ery pros - pect pleas - es, And on - ly man is vile?
Shall we to men be - night - ed The lamp of life de - ny?
Till, like a sea of glo - ry, It spreads from pole to pole:

From man-y an an - cient riv - er, From man-y a palm-y plain,
In vain with lav - ish kind - ness The gifts of God are strown;
Sal - va - tion! O sal - va - tion! The joy - ful sound pro - claim,
Till o'er our ran-somed na - ture The Lamb for sin - ners slain,

They call us to de - liv - er Their land from er - ror's chain.
The hea - then in his blind - ness Bows down to wood and stone.
Till earth's re - mot - est na - tion Has learned Mes - si - ah's name.
Re - deem - er, King, Cre - a - tor, In bliss re - turns to reign.

The Ninety and Nine

Elizabeth C. Clephane

Ira D. Sankey

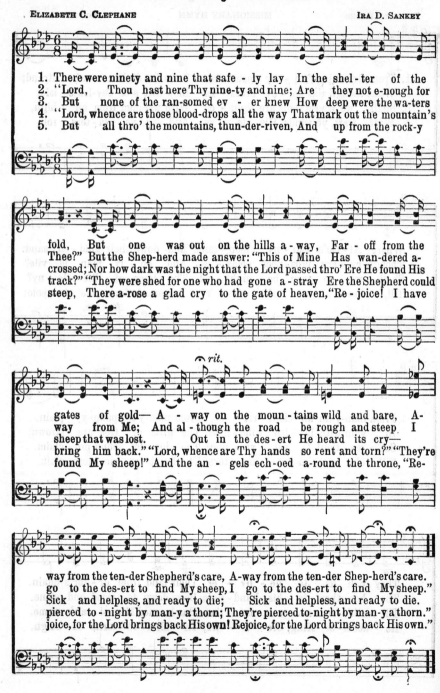

1. There were ninety and nine that safe - ly lay In the shel - ter of the
2. "Lord, Thou hast here Thy nine-ty and nine; Are they not e-nough for
3. But none of the ran-somed ev - er knew How deep were the wa-ters
4. "Lord, whence are those blood-drops all the way That mark out the mountain's
5. But all thro' the mountains, thun-der-riven, And up from the rock-y

fold, But one was out on the hills a - way, Far - off from the
Thee?" But the Shep-herd made answer: "This of Mine Has wan-dered a-
crossed; Nor how dark was the night that the Lord passed thro' Ere He found His
track?" "They were shed for one who had gone a - stray Ere the Shepherd could
steep, There a-rose a glad cry to the gate of heaven, "Re - joice! I have

rit.

gates of gold— A - way on the moun - tains wild and bare, A-
way from Me; And al - though the road be rough and steep I
sheep that was lost. Out in the des - ert He heard its cry—
bring him back." "Lord, whence are Thy hands so rent and torn?" "They're
found My sheep!" And the an - gels ech-oed a-round the throne, "Re-

way from the ten-der Shepherd's care, A-way from the ten-der Shep-herd's care.
go to the des-ert to find My sheep, I go to the des-ert to find My sheep."
Sick and helpless, and ready to die; Sick and helpless, and ready to die.
pierced to - night by man-y a thorn; They're pierced to-night by man-y a thorn."
joice, for the Lord brings back His own! Rejoice, for the Lord brings back His own."

There Is a Fountain

WILLIAM COWPER   CLEANSING FOUNTAIN   LOWELL MASON

1. There is   a foun-tain filled with blood Drawn from Im - man-uel's veins;
2. The dy - ing thief re - joiced to see That foun-tain in   his   day;
3. Dear dy - ing Lamb, Thy pre-cious blood Shall nev - er   lose its   power,
4. E'er since by faith I   saw the stream Thy flow-ing wounds sup - ply,
5. When this poor lisp-ing, stammering tongue Lies   si - lent in   the grave,

And sin-ners, plunged be-neath that flood, Lose all   their guilt - y   stains:
And there may I, though vile as he, Wash all   my   sins a - way:
Till all   the ran-somed Church of God Be saved, to sin   no   more:
Re - deem-ing love has been my theme, And shall be till   I   die:
Then in   a   no - bler, sweet - er song, I'll   sing Thy power to   save:

Lose all   their guilt - y   stains, Lose all   their guilt - y   stains;
Wash all   my   sins a - way, Wash all   my   sins a - way;
Be saved, to sin no · more, Be saved, to sin no   more;
And shall be till I   die, And shall be till I   die;
I'll   sing Thy power to   save, I'll   sing Thy power to   save;

And sin-ners, plunged be-neath that flood, Lose all   their guilt - y   stains.
And there may I, though vile   as he, Wash all   my   sins a - way.
Till all   the ran-somed Church of God Be saved, to sin   no   more.
Re - deem - ing love has been my theme, And shall be till   I   die.
Then in   a   no - bler, sweet - er song I'll   sing Thy power to save.

A Mighty Fortress

EIN' FESTE BURG

M. L.

Martin Luther

1. A might-y for-tress is our God, A bul-wark nev-er fail - ing;
2. Did we in our own strength confide, Our striv-ing would be los - ing,
3. And though this world, with devils filled, Should threaten to un - do us,
4. That word a - bove all earthly powers—No thanks to them—a - bid - eth;

Our help - er He, a - mid the flood Of mor - tal ills pre - vail - ing.
Were not the right Man on our side, The Man of God's own choos - ing.
We will not fear, for God hath willed His truth to tri - umph through us.
The Spir - it and the gifts are ours Thro' Him who with us sid - eth.

For still our an - cient foe Doth seek to work us woe; His craft and power
Dost ask who that may be? Christ Je - sus, it is He; Lord Sab-aoth is
The prince of darkness grim—We trem-ble not for him; His rage we can
Let goods and kin-dred go, This mor - tal life al - so; The bod - y they

are great, And, armed with cru-el hate, On earth is not his e - qual.
His name, From age to age the same, And He must win the bat - tle.
en - dure, For lo! his doom is sure: One lit - tle word shall fell him.
may kill; God's truth a - bid-eth still, His king-dom is for - ev - er.

America the Beautiful

KATHARINE LEE BATES   MATERNA   SAMUEL A. WARD

1. O beau-ti-ful for spa-cious skies, For am-ber waves of grain,
2. O beau-ti-ful for pil-grim feet, Whose stern, im-pas-sioned stress
3. O beau-ti-ful for he-roes proved In lib-er-at-ing strife,
4. O beau-ti-ful for pa-triot dream That sees be-yond the years

For pur-ple moun-tain maj-es-ties A-bove the fruit-ed plain!
A thor-ough-fare for free-dom beat A-cross the wil-der-ness!
Who more than self their coun-try loved, And mer-cy more than life!
Thine al-a-bas-ter cit-ies gleam, Un-dimmed by hu-man tears!

A-mer-i-ca! A-mer-i-ca! God shed His grace on thee,
A-mer-i-ca! A-mer-i-ca! God mend thine ev-ery flaw,
A-mer-i-ca! A-mer-i-ca! May God thy gold re-fine,
A-mer-i-ca! A-mer-i-ca! God shed His grace on thee,

And crown thy good with broth-er-hood From sea to shin-ing sea.
Con-firm thy soul in self-con-trol, Thy lib-er-ty in law.
Till all suc-cess be no-ble-ness, And ev-ery gain di-vine.
And crown thy good with broth-er-hood From sea to shin-ing sea.

78   At the Roll Call

Rev. W. C. POOLE

B. D. ACKLEY

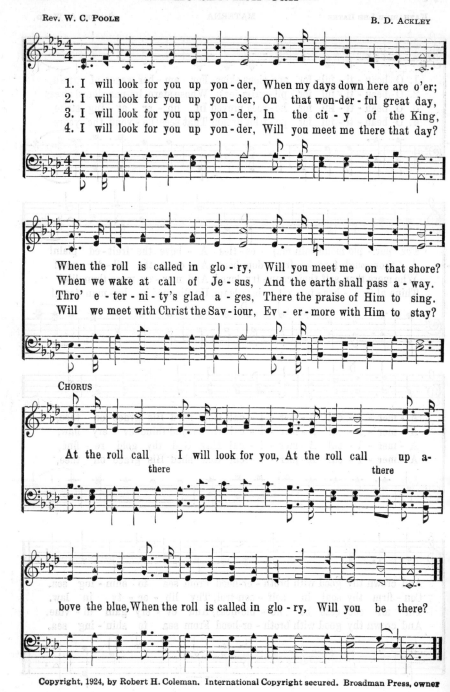

1. I will look for you up yon-der, When my days down here are o'er;
2. I will look for you up yon-der, On that won-der-ful great day,
3. I will look for you up yon-der, In the cit-y of the King,
4. I will look for you up yon-der, Will you meet me there that day?

When the roll is called in glo-ry, Will you meet me on that shore?
When we wake at call of Je-sus, And the earth shall pass a-way.
Thro' e-ter-ni-ty's glad a-ges, There the praise of Him to sing.
Will we meet with Christ the Sav-iour, Ev-er-more with Him to stay?

CHORUS

At the roll call there I will look for you, At the roll call there up a-
bove the blue, When the roll is called in glo-ry, Will you be there?

The Home Over There

D. W. C. HUNTINGTON   TULLIUS C. O'KANE

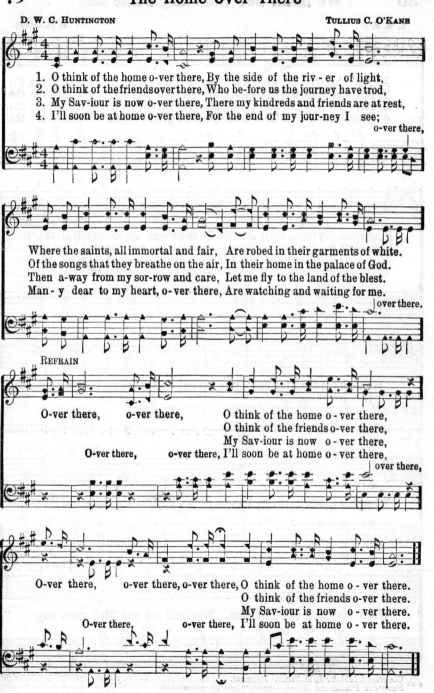

1. O think of the home o-ver there, By the side of the riv - er of light,
2. O think of the friends over there, Who be-fore us the journey have trod,
3. My Sav-iour is now o-ver there, There my kindreds and friends are at rest,
4. I'll soon be at home o-ver there, For the end of my jour-ney I see;

o-ver there,

Where the saints, all immortal and fair, Are robed in their garments of white.
Of the songs that they breathe on the air, In their home in the palace of God.
Then a-way from my sor-row and care, Let me fly to the land of the blest.
Man - y dear to my heart, o-ver there, Are watching and waiting for me.

over there.

REFRAIN

O-ver there,   o-ver there,   O think of the home o - ver there,
                              O think of the friends o - ver there,
                              My Sav-iour is now o - ver there,
O-ver there,   o-ver there, I'll soon be at home o - ver there,

over there,

O-ver there,   o-ver there, o-ver there, O think of the home o - ver there.
                               O think of the friends o - ver there.
                               My Sav-iour is now o - ver there.
O-ver there,   o-ver there, I'll soon be at home o - ver there.

80 We Shall See the King Some Day

L. E. J.

L. E. Jones

1. Tho' the way we jour-ney may be oft-en drear, We shall see the
2. Aft-er pain and an-guish, aft-er toil and care, We shall see the
3. Aft-er foes are con-quered, aft-er bat-tles won, We shall see the
4. There with all the loved ones who have gone be-fore, We shall see the

King some day (some day); On that bless-ed morn-ing clouds will dis-ap-pear;
King some day (some day); Thro' the end-less a-ges joy and bless-ing share,
King some day (some day); Aft-er strife is o-ver, aft-er set of sun,
King some day (some day); Sor-row past for-ev-er, on that peace-ful shore,

Chorus

We shall see the King some day. We shall see the King some day (some day),

When the clouds have rolled a-way (a-way); Gath-ered 'round the throne,

When He shall call His own, We shall see the King some day.

Stepping in the Light

Eliza E. Hewitt

William J. Kirkpatrick

1. Try - ing to walk in the steps of the Sav-iour, Try - ing to fol - low our
2. Press-ing more close-ly to Him who is lead-ing, When we are tempted to
3. Walk-ing in foot-steps of gen - tle for-bear-ance, Foot-steps of faith-ful-ness,
4. Try - ing to walk in the steps of the Sav-iour, Up-ward, still up-ward we'll

Sav - iour and King; Shap-ing our lives by His bless-ed ex-am-ple,
turn from the way; Trust-ing the arm that is strong to de-fend us,
mer - cy and love; Look-ing to Him for the grace free-ly prom-ised,
fol - low our Guide; When we shall see Him, "the King in His beau-ty,"

CHORUS

Hap-py, how hap-py, the songs that we bring.
Hap-py, how hap-py, our prais-es each day. How beau-ti-ful to walk in the
Hap-py, how hap-py, our jour-ney a-bove!
Hap-py, how hap-py, our place at His side!

steps of the Sav-iour, Step-ping in the light, Step-ping in the light; How

beau-ti-ful to walk in the steps of the Sav-iour, Led in paths of light!

82 No Longer Lonely

R. H.

ROBERT HARKNESS

1. On life's pathway I am nev-er lone-ly, My Lord is with me, my Lord di-
2. I shall not be lone-ly in my sor-row, He will sus-tain me un-til the
3. I shall not be lone-ly in the val-ley, Tho' shadows gath-er, I will not

vine;   Ev - er pre-sent Guide, I trust Him on - ly, No lon-ger
end;   Dark-est night He turns to brightest mor - row, No lon-ger
fear;   He has promised ev - er to up - hold me, No lon-ger

CHORUS

lone-ly, for He is mine. . .
lone-ly! He is my Friend. . No longer lone - ly, No longer lone - ly, For
lone-ly! He will be near. . .

Je - sus is the Friend of friends to me; . . No lon-ger lone - ly, No lon - ger
to me;

lone - ly, For Je - sus is the Friend of friends to me.
of friends to me.

He Lives On High

Words by
B. B. McKINNEY

Arr. by B. B. McKINNEY
From Hawaiin Folk Song

1. Christ the Sav - iour came from heaven's glo - ry, To re - deem the
2. He a - rose from death and all its sor - row, To dwell in that
3. Wea - ry soul, to Je - sus come con - fess - ing, Re - demp-tion from

lost from sin and shame; On His brow He wore the thorn-crown
land of joy and love; He is com - ing back some glad to-
sin He of - fers thee; Look to Je - sus and re - ceive a

go - ry, And up - on Cal - va - ry He took my blame.
mor - row, And He'll take all His chil-dren home a - bove.
bless - ing, There is life, there is joy and vic - to - ry.

CHORUS

He lives on high, He lives on high, Tri-um-phant o - ver sin and all its

stain; He lives on high, He lives on high, Some day He's com-ing a - gain.

Arr. Copyright, 1921, by Robet H. Coleman. Broadman Press, owner.

Once for All

P. P. B.

P. P. BLISS

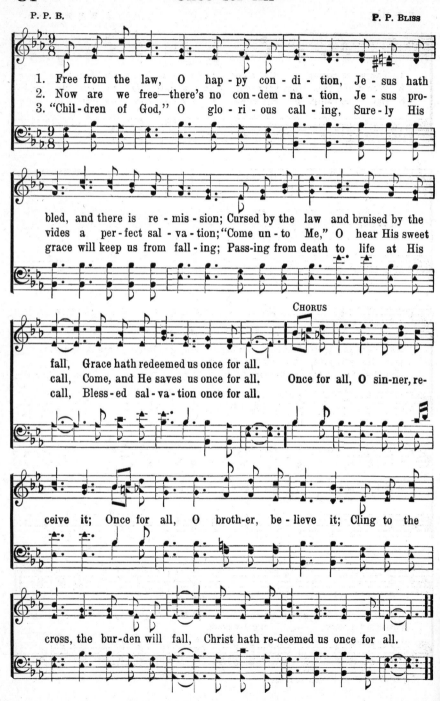

1. Free from the law, O hap-py con-di-tion, Je-sus hath
2. Now are we free—there's no con-dem-na-tion, Je-sus pro-
3. "Chil-dren of God," O glo-ri-ous call-ing, Sure-ly His

bled, and there is re-mis-sion; Cursed by the law and bruised by the
vides a per-fect sal-va-tion; "Come un-to Me," O hear His sweet
grace will keep us from fall-ing; Pass-ing from death to life at His

CHORUS

fall, Grace hath redeemed us once for all.
call, Come, and He saves us once for all.   Once for all, O sin-ner, re-
call, Bless-ed sal-va-tion once for all.

ceive it; Once for all, O broth-er, be-lieve it; Cling to the

cross, the bur-den will fall, Christ hath re-deemed us once for all.

85 Power in the Blood

B. B. McK.

B. B. McKinney

1. There is power in the blood Of the dear Lamb of God, Shed for
2. Would you turn from your sin, And the new life be - gin, Would you
3. Let us sing of His power, Ev - ery day, ev - ery hour, Let us

all on the cru - el tree; All who plunge 'neath its flow Shall be
have peace with - in your soul? Look to Je - sus and live, Life and
tell of His match-less love; Till our work is com-plete, And with

whit - er than snow, And from bondage of sin go free. There is power, . . .
joy He will give, Thro' His blood He will make you whole.
Christ we shall meet In that beau-ti - ful home a - bove.

CHORUS

Power in the blood,

might-y power, . . . There is power in the blood of the Lamb. . . . There is
power in the blood,

of the Lamb,

power, . . . might-y power . . . In the life-giv-ing blood of the Lamb.
Power in the blood, — might-y power,

86 Yield Not to Temptation

H. R. P.

Dr. H. R. PALMER

1. Yield not to temp-ta - tion, For yield-ing is sin; Each vic-tory will
2. Shun e - vil com-pan - ions, Bad lan-guage dis-dain; God's name hold in
3. To him that o'er-com - eth, God giv - eth a crown; Thro' faith we will

help you Some oth - er to win; Fight man - ful - ly on - ward,
rev-erence, Nor take it in vain; Be thought-ful and ear - nest,
con - quer, Though of-ten cast down; He who is our Sav - iour,

Dark pas-sions sub - due; Look ev - er to Je - sus, He'll car-ry you through.
Kind-heart-ed and true; Look ev - er to Je - sus, He'll car-ry you through.
Our strength will re-new; Look ev - er to Je - sus, He'll car-ry you through.

Chorus

Ask the Sav - iour to help you, Com - fort, strength-en, and keep you;

He is will - ing to aid you, He will car - ry you through.

87 Our Best

S. C. KIRK

GRANT COLFAX TULLAR

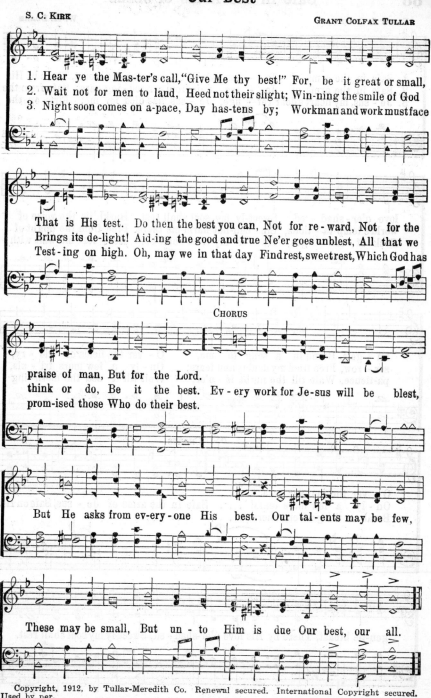

1. Hear ye the Mas-ter's call, "Give Me thy best!" For, be it great or small,
2. Wait not for men to laud, Heed not their slight; Win-ning the smile of God
3. Night soon comes on a-pace, Day has-tens by; Workman and work must face

That is His test. Do then the best you can, Not for re-ward, Not for the
Brings its de-light! Aid-ing the good and true Ne'er goes unblest, All that we
Test-ing on high. Oh, may we in that day Find rest, sweet rest, Which God has

CHORUS

praise of man, But for the Lord.
think or do, Be it the best. Ev-ery work for Je-sus will be blest,
prom-ised those Who do their best.

But He asks from ev-ery-one His best. Our tal-ents may be few,

These may be small, But un-to Him is due Our best, our all.

Safe in the Arms of Jesus

BY J. CROSBY

W. H. DOANE

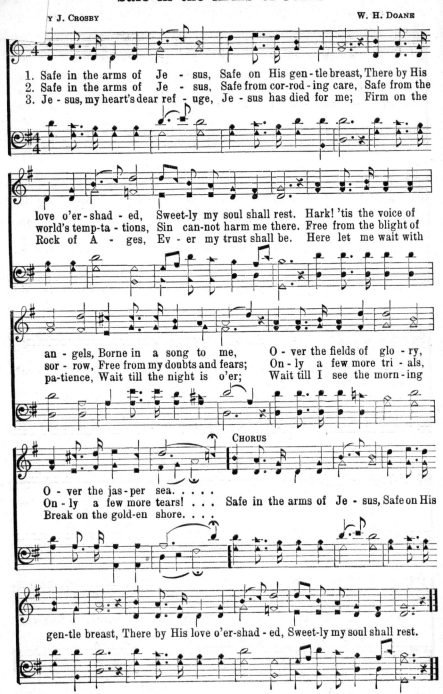

1. Safe in the arms of Je - sus, Safe on His gen - tle breast, There by His
2. Safe in the arms of Je - sus, Safe from cor-rod - ing care, Safe from the
3. Je - sus, my heart's dear ref - uge, Je - sus has died for me; Firm on the

love o'er - shad - ed, Sweet-ly my soul shall rest. Hark! 'tis the voice of
world's temp-ta - tions, Sin can-not harm me there. Free from the blight of
Rock of A - ges, Ev - er my trust shall be. Here let me wait with

an - gels, Borne in a song to me, O - ver the fields of glo - ry,
sor - row, Free from my doubts and fears; On - ly a few more tri - als,
pa-tience, Wait till the night is o'er; Wait till I see the morn - ing

O - ver the jas - per sea. . . . .
On - ly a few more tears! . . . Safe in the arms of Je - sus, Safe on His
Break on the gold-en shore. . . .

CHORUS

gen-tle breast, There by His love o'er-shad - ed, Sweet-ly my soul shall rest.

89 Sweet By and By

S. F. BENNETT

J. P. WEBSTER

1. There's a land that is fair-er than day, And by faith we can see it a-far; For the Fa-ther waits o-ver the way, To pre-pare us a dwell-ing-place there.
2. We shall sing on that beau-ti-ful shore The me-lo-di-ous songs of the blest, And our spir-its shall sor-row no more, Not a sigh for the bless-ing of rest.
3. To our boun-ti-ful Fa-ther a-bove, We will of-fer the trib-ute of praise, For the glo-ri-ous gift of His love, And the bless-ings that hal-low our days.

CHORUS

In the sweet by and by, We shall meet on that beau-ti-ful shore; In the sweet by and by, We shall meet on that beau-ti-ful shore.

Jesus My Lord Is Real to Me

R.

I. E. REYNOLDS

1. Je - sus my Lord is real to me, Day - time or when the
2. Je - sus my Lord is real to me, Com - fort - er true in
3. Je - sus my Lord is real to me, When I am tempt - ed

night shades fall, Wheth - er on land or storm - y sea—
sor - row's hour, Shares in my joys, what - e'er they be—
He is there, Helps me to live, my du - ty see—

He is my Friend, my All in all.
He is my Friend, to Him I bow.
He is my Friend, His cross I'll bear.

CHORUS

Je - sus my Lord is

real to me, Con - stant and true, lov - ing is He; Al - ways He's

near with words of good cheer, Je - sus my Lord is real to me.

91 The Kingdom Is Coming

Mrs. M. B. C. Slade

R. M. McIntosh

1. From all the dark plac-es Of earth's hea-then rac-es, O see how the thick shad-ows fly! The voice of sal-va-tion A-wakes ev-ery na-tion, Come o-ver and help us, they cry.

2. The sun-light is glanc-ing O'er ar-mies ad-vanc-ing, To con-quer the king-doms of sin; Our Lord shall possess them, His presence shall bless them, His beau-ty shall en-ter them in.

3. With shout-ing and sing-ing, And ju-bi-lant ring-ing, Their arms of re-bel-lion cast down; At last ev-ery na-tion The Lord of sal-va-tion Their King and Re-deem-er shall crown!

CHORUS

The king-dom is com-ing, O tell ye the sto-ry, God's ban-ner ex-alt-ed shall be! The earth shall be full of His knowledge and glo-ry, As wa-ters that cov-er the sea.

Jesus Lifted Me

B. B. McK.   B. B. McKinney

UNISON OR SOLO

1. I was sink-ing down in sin, Help-less as could be, . .
2. From a life of dark de-spair, From a rag-ing sea, . .
3. To a home of end-less love, With Him-self to be, . .

When with might-y hands of love Je-sus lift-ed me! . .
From my sin and lost es-tate Je-sus lift-ed me! . .
To e-ter-nal life and peace Je-sus lift-ed me! . .

CHORUS

Je-sus lift-ed me, Je-sus lift-ed me, . .
e-ven me, e-ven me,

O what won-drous love so free! Je-sus lift-ed me!

93 Speak to My Heart

GENE ROUTH

B. B. McKINNEY

1. Speak to my heart, Lord Je - sus, Speak that my soul may hear;
2. Speak to my heart, Lord Je - sus, Purge me from ev - ery sin;
3. Speak to my heart, Lord Je - sus, It is no lon - ger mine;

Speak to my heart, Lord Je - sus, Calm ev - ery doubt and fear.
Speak to my heart, Lord Je - sus, Help me the lost to win.
Speak to my heart, Lord Je - sus, I would be whol - ly Thine.

CHORUS

Speak to my heart, oh, speak to my heart, Speak to my heart, I pray;

Yield - ed and still, seek - ing Thy will, Oh, speak to my heart to - day.

He Is Able to Deliver Thee

W. A. O.

WILLIAM A. OGDEN

1. 'Tis the grandest theme thro' the a - ges rung; 'Tis the grandest theme for a
2. 'Tis the grandest theme in the earth or main; 'Tis the grandest theme for a
3. 'Tis the grandest theme, let the ti - dings roll To the guilt-y heart, to the

mor - tal tongue; 'Tis the grand-est theme that the world e'er sung, "Our
mor - tal strain; 'Tis the grand-est theme, tell the world a - gain, "Our
sin - ful soul; Look to God in faith, He will make thee whole;"Our

CHORUS

God is a - ble to de - liv - er thee." He is a - - - ble to de-
a - ble, He is a - ble

liv - er thee, He is a - - - ble to de - liv - er thee; Tho' by
a - ble, He is a - ble

sin op-prest, Go to Him for rest; "Our God is a - ble to de - liv - er thee."

95 A Friend of Mine

B. B. McK.   B. B. McKinney

1. There is joy in my heart as I jour-ney To the cit-y of
2. Tho' the world may de-spise and dis-own me, And the sun may re-
3. I will work, watch and pray for my Sav-ior, I will fol-low His

love di-vine, And I sing o'er and o'er the sweet sto-ry,
fuse to shine, There is One who will nev-er for-sake me,
wise de-sign, Till He calls me to meet Him in Glo-ry;

Chorus

Je-sus is a Friend of mine. Je-sus, Je-sus

is a Friend of mine, Je-sus, Je-sus is a Friend di-vine; In my

heart He makes the sun to shine, Je-sus is a Friend of mine.

96 Living for Jesus

T. O. Chisholm

C. Harold Lowden

Not fast

1. Liv-ing for Je-sus a life that is true, Striv-ing to please Him in all that I do,
2. Liv-ing for Je-sus who died in my place, Bear-ing on Cal-v'ry my sin and dis-grace,
3. Liv-ing for Je-sus wher-ev-er I am, Do-ing each du-ty in His ho-ly name,
4. Liv-ing for Je-sus thro' earth's lit-tle while, My dear-est treas-ure, the light of His smile,

Yield-ing al-le-giance, glad-heart-ed and free, This is the path-way of bless-ing for me.
Such love constrains me to an-swer His call, Fol-low His lead-ing and give Him my all.
Will-ing to suf-fer af-flic-tion or loss, Deem-ing each tri-al a part of my cross.
Seek-ing the lost ones He died to re-deem, Bring-ing the wea-ry to find rest in Him.

CHORUS Unison. A little slower

O Je-sus, Lord and Sav-iour, I give my-self to Thee; For Thou, in Thy a-

tone-ment, Didst give Thy-self for me; I own no oth-er Mas-ter, My

rit.

heart shall be Thy throne, My life I give, henceforth to live, O Christ, for Thee a-lone.

*Melody in lower notes. A two-part effect may be had by having the men sing the melody, the women taking the middle notes.

97 Satisfied with Jesus

B. B. McK.　　　　　　　　　　　　　　　　　　　　　　B. B. McKinney

1. I am sat-is-fied with Je-sus, He has done so much for me,
2. He is with me in my tri-als, Best of friends of all is He;
3. I can hear the voice of Je-sus Call-ing out so plead-ing-ly,
4. When my work on earth is end-ed, And I cross the mys-tic sea,

He has suf-fered to re-deem me, He has died to set me free.
I can al-ways count on Je-sus, Can He al-ways count on me?
"Go and win the lost and stray-ing;" Is He sat-is-fied with me?
Oh, that I could hear Him say-ing, "I am sat-is-fied with thee."

CHORUS

I am sat-is-fied, I am sat-is-fied, I am sat-is-fied with Je-sus, But the ques-tion comes to me, As I think of Cal-va-ry, Is my Mas-ter sat-is-fied with me?

98 There Is a Green Hill Far Away

Cecil F. Alexander

Geo. C. Stebbins

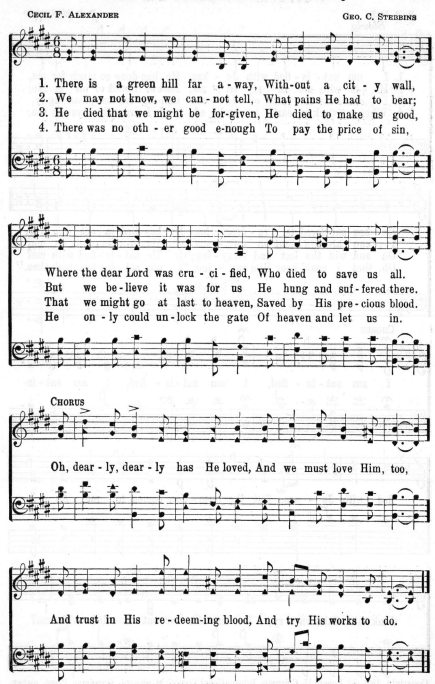

1. There is a green hill far a-way, With-out a cit-y wall,
2. We may not know, we can-not tell, What pains He had to bear;
3. He died that we might be for-given, He died to make us good,
4. There was no oth-er good e-nough To pay the price of sin,

Where the dear Lord was cru-ci-fied, Who died to save us all.
But we be-lieve it was for us He hung and suf-fered there.
That we might go at last to heaven, Saved by His pre-cious blood.
He on-ly could un-lock the gate Of heaven and let us in.

CHORUS

Oh, dear-ly, dear-ly has He loved, And we must love Him, too,

And trust in His re-deem-ing blood, And try His works to do.

99 Wherever He Leads I'll Go

B. B. McK.   B. B. McKinney

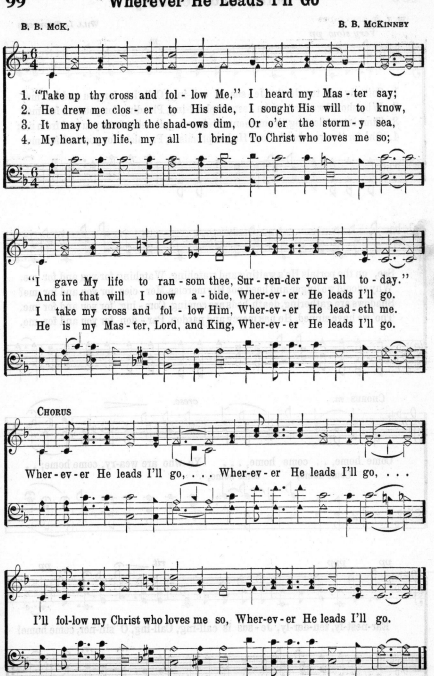

1. "Take up thy cross and fol-low Me," I heard my Mas-ter say;
2. He drew me clos-er to His side, I sought His will to know,
3. It may be through the shad-ows dim, Or o'er the storm-y sea,
4. My heart, my life, my all I bring To Christ who loves me so;

"I gave My life to ran-som thee, Sur-ren-der your all to-day."
And in that will I now a-bide, Wher-ev-er He leads I'll go.
I take my cross and fol-low Him, Wher-ev-er He lead-eth me.
He is my Mas-ter, Lord, and King, Wher-ev-er He leads I'll go.

CHORUS

Wher-ev-er He leads I'll go, . . . Wher-ev-er He leads I'll go, . . .

I'll fol-low my Christ who loves me so, Wher-ev-er He leads I'll go.

100 Softly and Tenderly

W. L. T.

WILL L. THOMPSON

Very slow pp

1. Soft - ly and ten-der-ly Je - sus is call-ing, Call-ing for you and for me;
2. Why should we tarry when Jesus is plead-ing, Pleading for you and for me?
3. Time is now fleeting, the moments are passing, Passing from you and from me;
4. Oh! for the won-der-ful love He has promised, Promised for you and for me;

See, on the portals He's waiting and watching, Watching for you and for me.
Why should we linger and heed not His mercies, Mer - cies for you and for me?
Shadows are gathering, death-beds are coming, Com - ing for you and for me.
Tho' we have sinned, He has mercy and pardon, Par - don for you and for me.

CHORUS *m*   *cresc.*

Come home, .. come home, ... Ye who are wea-ry, come home; ..
Come home,   come home,

pp   ppp   rit.   pp

Ear-nest-ly, ten-der-ly, Je - sus is call-ing, Call-ing, O sin-ner, come home!

101   What Will You Do with Jesus?

B. B. McK.
Chorus Anonymous

B. B. McKINNEY

SOLO *Slowly*

1. Je - sus is stand-ing at your heart's door, Stand-ing and
2. At your sad heart He is knock-ing still, Long-ing to
3. Oh, will you leave Him a - lone, out - side? Or will you
4. Will you now an - swer His ten - der call? Will you o-

knock-ing, He's knocked be-fore; This is the ques-tion you face once more:
en - ter, your soul to thrill; You must ac-cept or re - ject His will:
choose Him what-e'er be - tide? This is the ques-tion you must de - cide:
bey Him what-e'er be - fall? Fol-low Him dai - ly as Lord of all?

CHORUS

What will you do with Je - sus? What will you do with
Je - sus? Neu-tral you can - not be; ... Some day your

rit.

heart will be ask - ing: "What will He do with me?"

102 All On the Altar

Dedicated to young people. B. B. McK.

B. B. McK.

B. B. McKINNEY

1. All on the al-tar, dear Je-sus, Mas-ter, I hear Thy call; ...
2. All on the al-tar, dear Je-sus, Yield-ed am I to Thee; ..
3. All on the al-tar, dear Je-sus, On-ly Thy will is mine; ..
4. All on the al-tar, dear Je-sus, All at Thy feet I lay; ...

Somewhere I know Thou canst use me, I must sur-ren-der my all. ....
Take me and mold me and make me As Thou wouldst have me be. ....
Let my lips tell the sweet sto-ry, Tell of Thy love di-vine. ...
Will-ing to toil and to suf-fer, "Thro'-out life's lit-tle day." ..

CHORUS.

My all for Thee, my all for Thee, Who gave Thine all, dear Lord, for me;
My all for Thee, for Thee, Who gave Thine all for me;

rit.

Thy will di-vine, Henceforth is mine, To live for Thee, dear Saviour, for Thee.
Thy will di-vine is mine,

103 I Surrender All

J. W. Van DeVenter

W. S. Weeden

1. All to Jesus I surrender, All to Him I freely give;
2. All to Jesus I surrender, Humbly at His feet I bow;
3. All to Jesus I surrender, Make me, Saviour, wholly Thine;
4. All to Jesus I surrender, Lord, I give myself to Thee;

I will ever love and trust Him, In His presence daily live.
Worldly pleasures all forsaken, Take me, Jesus, take me now.
Let me feel the Holy Spirit,—Truly know that Thou art mine.
Fill me with Thy love and power, Let Thy blessing fall on me.

Chorus

I surrender all,
I surrender all,
I surrender all;
I surrender all;

All to Thee, my blessed Saviour, I surrender all.

104 Trust and Obey

J. H. SAMMIS

D. B. TOWNER

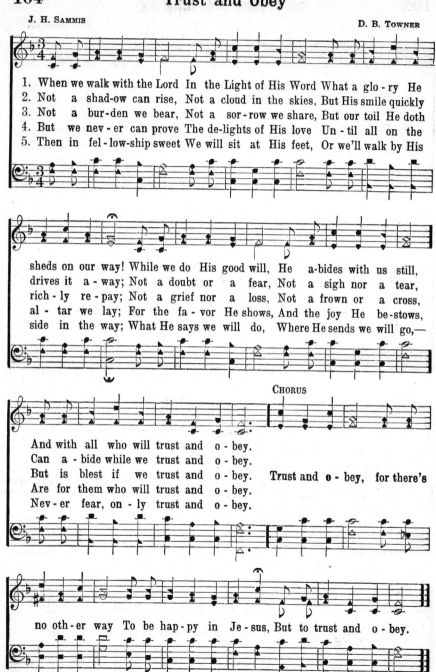

1. When we walk with the Lord In the Light of His Word What a glo-ry He
2. Not a shad-ow can rise, Not a cloud in the skies, But His smile quickly
3. Not a bur-den we bear, Not a sor-row we share, But our toil He doth
4. But we nev-er can prove The de-lights of His love Un-til all on the
5. Then in fel-low-ship sweet We will sit at His feet, Or we'll walk by His

sheds on our way! While we do His good will, He a-bides with us still,
drives it a-way; Not a doubt or a fear, Not a sigh nor a tear,
rich-ly re-pay; Not a grief nor a loss, Not a frown or a cross,
al-tar we lay; For the fa-vor He shows, And the joy He be-stows,
side in the way; What He says we will do, Where He sends we will go,—

CHORUS

And with all who will trust and o-bey.
Can a-bide while we trust and o-bey.
But is blest if we trust and o-bey.   Trust and o-bey, for there's
Are for them who will trust and o-bey.
Nev-er fear, on-ly trust and o-bey.

no oth-er way To be hap-py in Je-sus, But to trust and o-bey.

105 He Keeps Me Singing

L. B. B.

L. B. BRIDGERS

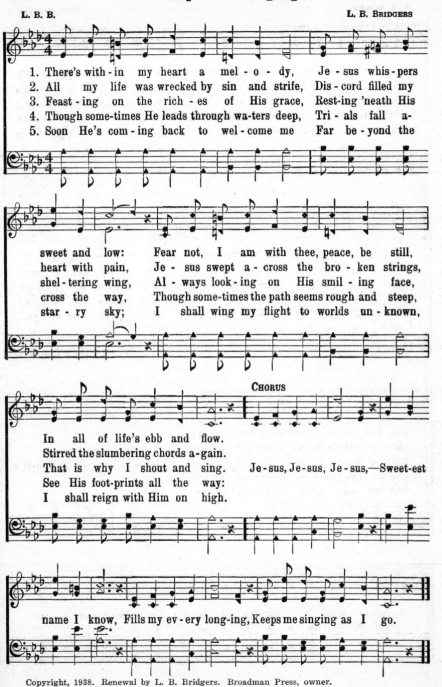

1. There's with-in my heart a mel-o-dy, Je-sus whis-pers
2. All my life was wrecked by sin and strife, Dis-cord filled my
3. Feast-ing on the rich-es of His grace, Rest-ing 'neath His
4. Though some-times He leads through wa-ters deep, Tri-als fall a-
5. Soon He's com-ing back to wel-come me Far be-yond the

sweet and low: Fear not, I am with thee, peace, be still,
heart with pain, Je-sus swept a-cross the bro-ken strings,
shel-tering wing, Al-ways look-ing on His smil-ing face,
cross the way, Though some-times the path seems rough and steep,
star-ry sky; I shall wing my flight to worlds un-known,

CHORUS

In all of life's ebb and flow.
Stirred the slumbering chords a-gain.
That is why I shout and sing. Je-sus, Je-sus, Je-sus,—Sweet-est
See His foot-prints all the way:
I shall reign with Him on high.

name I know, Fills my ev-ery long-ing, Keeps me singing as I go.

My Redeemer

P. P. BLISS   JAMES MCGRANAHAN

1. I will sing of my Re-deem-er And His won-drous love to me;
2. I will tell the won-drous sto-ry, How my lost es-tate to save,
3. I will praise my dear Re-deem-er, His tri-um-phant power I'll tell,
4. I will sing of my Re-deem-er, And His heaven-ly love to me;

On the cru-el cross He suf-fered, From the curse to set me free.
In His bound-less love and mer-cy, He the ran-som free-ly gave.
How the vic-to-ry He giv-eth O-ver sin, and death, and hell.
He from death to life hath brought me, Son of God, with Him to be.

CHORUS

Sing, oh, sing . . . . of my Re-deem-er, With His
Sing, oh, sing of my Re-deem-er, Sing, oh, sing of my Re-deem-er, With His

blood . . . . He pur-chased me, ... On the cross . . . . He sealed my
blood He purchased me, With His blood He purchased me, On the cross He sealed my pardon, On the

Repeat pp after last verse

par-don, Paid the debt . . . . and made me free. . . . .
cross He sealed my par-don, Paid the debt and made me free, and made me free.

107   Thy Word Have I Hid In My Heart

Adapted by E. O. S.

E. O. SELLERS

1. Thy Word is a lamp to my feet, A light to my path al-way;
2. For-ev-er, O Lord, is Thy Word Es-tab-lished and fixed on high;
3. At morn-ing, at noon, and at night I ev-er will give Thee praise;
4. Thro' Him whom Thy Word hath foretold, The Sav-iour and Morn-ing Star,

To guide and to save me from sin, And show me the heaven-ly way.
Thy faith-ful-ness un-to all men A-bid-eth for-ev-er nigh.
For Thou art my por-tion, O Lord, And shall be through all my days!
Sal-va-tion and peace have been bro't To those who have strayed a-far.

CHORUS—Ps. 119: 11

Thy Word have I hid in my heart, ... That I might not
in my heart,

sin a-gainst Thee, ... That I might not sin, That
a-gainst Thee,

ad lib.

I might not sin, Thy Word have I hid in my heart.

108 Thanks Be to God

B. B. McK.

B. B. McKinney

1. Thanks be to God for life and light For love and joy and
2. Thanks be to God for Christ our King, For peace and calm that
3. Thanks be to God for food and care, For Chris-tian home and
4. Thanks be to God for heav'n and home, Far, far be-yond the

sun-shine bright; For grace to lead us thro' the night, Thanks be to
He doth bring; For strength to suf-fer and to sing, Thanks be to
friendships rare; For Bi-ble truth and dai-ly prayer, Thanks be to
star-ry dome; Where saved ones meet no more to roam, Thanks be to

CHORUS

God, thanks be to God! Thanks be to God, thanks be to God! For
wood-land and mead-ow for life-giv-ing sod, For bless-ings un-
numbered, o'er paths we have trod, Thanks be to God, thanks be to God!

109 Sunshine in the Soul

E. E. Hewitt

John R. Sweney

1. There's sun-shine in my soul to-day, More glo-ri-ous and bright
2. There's mu-sic in my soul to-day, A car-ol to my King,
3. There's springtime in my soul to-day, For, when the Lord is near,
4. There's glad-ness in my soul to-day, And hope and praise and love,

Than glows in an-y earth-ly sky, For Je-sus is my light.
And Je-sus, lis-ten-ing, can hear The songs I can-not sing.
The dove of peace sings in my heart, The flow'rs of grace ap-pear.
For bless-ings which He gives me now, For joys "laid up" a-bove.

REFRAIN

O there's sun - - - shine, bless-ed sun - - shine,
O there's sun-shine in my soul, bless-ed sun-shine in my soul,

While the peace-ful, hap-py mo-ments roll;
hap-py mo-ments roll;

When

Je-sus shows His smil-ing face, There is sun-shine in my soul.

110 Is Your All on the Altar?

E. A. H.

ELISHA A. HOFFMAN

1. You have longed for sweet peace, and for faith to in-crease, And have ear-nest-ly
2. Would you walk with the Lord, in the light of His Word, And have peace and con-
3. Oh, we nev - er can know what the Lord will be-stow Of the bless-ings for
4. Who can tell all the love He will send from a - bove, And how hap - py our

fer - vent-ly prayed; But you can-not have rest or be per - fect-ly blest
tent-ment al - way, You must do His sweet will, to be free from all ill,
which we have prayed, Till our bod - y and soul He doth ful - ly con-trol,
hearts will be made, Of the fel - low-ship sweet we shall share at His feet,

CHORUS

Un - til all on the al - tar is laid.
On the al - tar your all you must lay.   Is your all on the al - tar of
And our all on the al - tar is laid.
When our all on the al - tar is laid.

sac - ri - fice laid? Your heart, does the Spir - it con - trol? . . . You can on - ly be

blest and have peace and sweet rest, As you yield Him your bod - y and soul.

111 Are You Washed in the Blood?

E. A. H.

ELISHA A. HOFFMAN

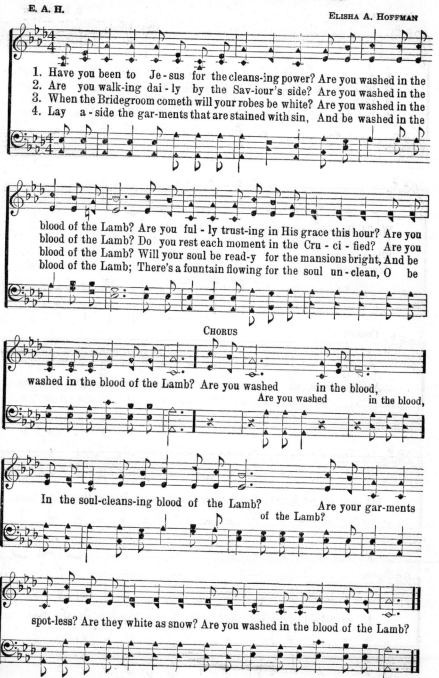

1. Have you been to Jesus for the cleansing power? Are you washed in the blood of the Lamb? Are you fully trusting in His grace this hour? Are you
2. Are you walking daily by the Saviour's side? Are you washed in the blood of the Lamb? Do you rest each moment in the Crucified? Are you
3. When the Bridegroom cometh will your robes be white? Are you washed in the blood of the Lamb? Will your soul be ready for the mansions bright, And be
4. Lay aside the garments that are stained with sin, And be washed in the blood of the Lamb; There's a fountain flowing for the soul unclean, O be

CHORUS

washed in the blood of the Lamb? Are you washed in the blood,
Are you washed in the blood,
In the soul-cleansing blood of the Lamb? Are your garments
of the Lamb?
spot-less? Are they white as snow? Are you washed in the blood of the Lamb?

112 At the Cross

ISAAC WATTS

R. E. HUDSON

1. A - las, and did my Sav - iour bleed? And did my Sov-ereign die?
2. Was it for crimes that I have done, He groaned up-on the tree?
3. Well might the sun in dark - ness hide, And shut his glo - ries in,
4. But drops of grief can ne'er re - pay The debt of love I owe:

Would He de - vote that sa - cred head For such a worm as I?
A - maz - ing pit - y! grace un-known! And love be - yond de - gree!
When Christ, the might - y Mak - er, died For man the crea-ture's sin.
Here, Lord, I give my - self a - way, 'Tis all that I can do!

CHORUS

At the cross, at the cross where I first saw the light, And the

bur - den of my heart rolled a - way (rolled a-way), It was there by faith

I re - ceived my sight, And now I am hap - py all the day!

113 Christ Receiveth Sinful Men

Arr. from NEUMASTER

JAMES McGRANAHAN

1. Sin - ners Je - sus will re - ceive; Sound this word of grace to all
2. Come, and He will give you rest; Trust Him, for His word is plain;
3. Now my heart con-demns me not, Pure be - fore the law I stand;
4. Christ re-ceiv-eth sin - ful men, E - ven me with all my sin;

Who the heaven-ly path-way leave, All who lin - ger, all who fall.
He will take the sin - ful-est; Christ re - ceiv-eth sin - ful men.
He who cleansed me from all spot, Sat - is-fied its last de-mand.
Purged from ev - ery spot and stain, Heaven with Him I en - ter in.

REFRAIN

Sing it o'er . . . . . and o'er a-gain; . . . . Christ re-
Sing it o'er a-gain, Sing it o'er a-gain; Christ re-

ceiv - - - eth sin-ful men; . . . Make the mes - - - sage
ceiv-eth sin-ful men, Christ re-ceiv-eth sin-ful men; Make the mes-sage plain,

clear and plain: . . . . Christ re - ceiv - eth sin - ful men.
Make the mes-sage plain: Christ re - ceiv - eth

Love Is the Theme

To my friend, L. E. Jones

A. C. F.

ALBERT C. FISHER

1. Of the themes that men have known, One su-preme-ly stands a - lone; ..
2. Let the bells of heav-en ring, Let the saints their trib - ute bring, ..
3. Since the Lord my soul un - bound, I am tell - ing all a - round ..
*4. As of old when blind and lame To the bless - ed Mas - ter came, ..

Thro' the a - ges it has shown,—'Tis His won-der-ful, won-der-ful love.
Let the world true prais-es sing For His won-der-ful, won-der-ful love.
Par - don, peace and joy are found In His won-der-ful, won-der-ful love.
Sin - ners, call ye on His name,— Trust His wonderful, won-der-ful love.

CHORUS

Love is the theme, Love is su-preme; Sweeter it grows; Glo - ry be-stows;

Bright as the sun Ev - er it glows! Love is the theme, E - ter - nal theme!

115 Wonderful Man of Galilee

B. B. McK.

B. B. McKinney.

1. I met Him one day on a lone-ly road, The Christ of Gal - i - lee;
2. I yield-ed my life to Him that day, To Christ of Gal - i - lee;
3. He gives me a song that none other can give, This Man of Gal - i - lee;
4. Some day He is com-ing a-gain for me, This Man of Gal - i - lee;

'Twas there that He lift-ed my heav-y load, This Man of Gal - i - lee.
He's walk-ing with me all a-long the way, This Man of Gal - i - lee.
I'll hon-or and serve Him each day I live, This Man of Gal - i - lee.
Transformed in His beau-ty, His face I'll see, This Man of Gal - i - lee.

CHORUS

Won-der-ful Man of Gal - i - lee, Won-der-ful Man of Gal - i - lee;

He's dear-er than all the world to me, This won-der-ful Man of Gal - i - lee.

116 Wonderful Peace of My Saviour

Rev. Alfred Barratt

I. E. Reynolds

SOLO OR DUET

1. Like ra - di - ant sun-shine that comes aft - er rain, Like beau - ti - ful
2. So soft and re-fresh-ing, as sweet as the dew, A prom - ise that
3. It bright-ens earth's dark-ness and ban - ish - es care, And helps you to
4. A guard-ian in dan - ger where e - vil is rife, A might - y de-

rest aft - er sor-row and pain, Like hope that is kin-dled re-turn-ing a - gain,
can-not be bro-ken to you; A light that will shine all the long journey through,
car - ry the bur-dens you bear; A ref - uge in trou-ble, your sor-rows to share,
fend-er in con-flict and strife, A beau - ti - ful guide to that heav-en-ly life,

Is the won - der - ful peace of my Sav - iour.

CHORUS

Won-der-ful peace, beau - ti - ful peace, Won-der-ful peace of my Sav - iour; There's nothing on earth can such gladness im - part As this won-der-ful peace of my Sav - iour.

117 Send the Light

C. H. G.

CHAS. H. GABRIEL

1. There's a call comes ring-ing o'er the rest-less wave, "Send the light! . . .
2. We have heard the Mac-e-do-nian call to-day, "Send the light! . . .
3. Let us pray that grace may ev-ery-where a-bound; Send the light! . . .
4. Let us not grow wea-ry in the work of love, Send the light! . . .

Send the light!

Send the light!" There are souls to res-cue, there are souls to save,
Send the light!" And a gold-en of-fering at the cross we lay,
Send the light! And a Christ-like spir-it ev-ery-where be found,
Send the light! Let us gath-er jew-els for a crown a-bove,

Send the light!

REFRAIN

Send the light! . . . Send the light! . . . Send the light! . . . the
Send the light! Send the light! Send the light!

bless-ed gos - pel light; Let it shine . . . . from shore to
the bless-ed gos-pel light; Let it shine

shore! . . . . . shine . . . . for-ev-er-more. . . . .
from shore to shore! Let it shine for-ev-er-more.

118 Jesus, Lover of My Soul

CHARLES WESLEY

S. B. MARSH
FINE.

1. Je - sus, Lov - er of my soul, Let me to Thy bos - om fly,
   While the near - er wa - ters roll, While the tem - pest still is high!

2. Oth - er ref - uge have I none; Hangs my help-less soul on Thee:
   Leave, ah, leave me not a - lone, Still sup-port and com - fort me!

3. Plen-teous grace with Thee is found, Grace to cov - er all my sin;
   Let the heal-ing streams a-bound, Make and keep me pure with - in.

D.C.—Safe in - to the ha - ven guide, O re-ceive my soul at last!
D.C.—Cov - er my de-fense-less head With the shad-ow of Thy wing.
D.C.—Spring Thou up with-in my heart, Rise to all e - ter - ni - ty.

D.C.

Hide me, O my Sav-iour, hide, Till the storm of life is past;
All my trust on Thee is stayed, All my help from Thee I bring;
Thou of life the foun - tain art; Free-ly let me take of Thee;

119 Come, Holy Spirit, Heavenly Dove

ISAAC WATTS

R. SIMPSON

1. Come, Ho - ly Spir - it, heaven-ly Dove, With all thy quickening powers,
2. Look! how we grov - el here be - low, Fond of these earth-ly toys;
3. Dear Lord, and shall we ev - er live At this poor dy - ing rate,
4. Come, Ho - ly Spir - it, heaven-ly Dove, With all thy quickening powers;

Kin - dle a flame of sa - cred love In these cold hearts of ours.
Our souls can nei - ther fly nor go To reach e - ter - nal joys.
Our love so faint, so cold to Thee, And Thine to us so great?
Come, shed a - broad a Sav-iour's love, And that shall kin - dle ours.

All Hail the Power

OLIVER HOLDEN

1. All hail the pow'r of Je - sus' name! Let an - gels pros - trate fall;
2. Ye cho - sen seed of Is - rael's race, Ye ran - somed from the fall,
3. Let ev - 'ry kin - dred, ev - 'ry tribe On this ter - res - trial ball,

Bring forth the roy - al di - a - dem, And crown Him Lord of all,
Hail Him who saves you by His grace, And crown Him Lord of all,
To Him all maj - es - ty as - cribe, And crown Him Lord of all,

Bring forth the roy - al di - a - dem, And crown Him Lord of all!
Hail Him who saves you by His grace, And crown Him Lord of all!
To Him all maj - es - ty as - cribe, And crown Him Lord of all!

121 [Second Tune]   MILES' LANE. C. M.   WILLIAM SHRUBSOLE

1. All hail the pow'r of Je - sus' name! Let an - gels pros - trate fall; Bring forth the roy - al

di - a - dem, And crown Him, crown Him, crown Him, Crown Him Lord of all!

122 O Worship the King

Robert Grant   LYONS   J. Michael Haydn

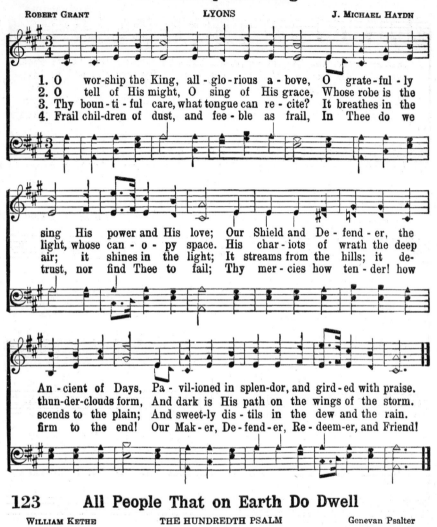

1. O wor-ship the King, all-glo-rious a-bove, O grate-ful-ly
2. O tell of His might, O sing of His grace, Whose robe is the
3. Thy boun-ti-ful care, what tongue can re-cite? It breathes in the
4. Frail chil-dren of dust, and fee-ble as frail, In Thee do we

sing His power and His love; Our Shield and De-fend-er, the
light, whose can-o-py space. His char-iots of wrath the deep
air; it shines in the light; It streams from the hills; it de-
trust, nor find Thee to fail; Thy mer-cies how ten-der! how

An-cient of Days, Pa-vil-ioned in splen-dor, and gird-ed with praise.
thun-der-clouds form, And dark is His path on the wings of the storm.
scends to the plain; And sweet-ly dis-tils in the dew and the rain.
firm to the end! Our Mak-er, De-fend-er, Re-deem-er, and Friend!

123 All People That on Earth Do Dwell

William Kethe   THE HUNDREDTH PSALM   Genevan Psalter

1. All peo-ple that on earth do dwell, Sing to the Lord with cheer-ful voice;
2. Know that the Lord is God in-deed; With-out our aid He did us make;
3. O en-ter then His gates with praise, Ap-proach with joy His courts un-to;
4. For why? the Lord our God is good; His mer-cy is for-ev-er sure;

Praise God, from whom all bless-ings flow; Praise Him, all creatures here be-low;

All People That on Earth Do Dwell

Him serve with fear, His praise forth tell; Come ye be-fore Him and re-joice.
We are His flock, He doth us feed, And for His sheep He doth us take.
Praise, laud, and bless His name al-ways, For it is seem-ly so to do.
His truth at all times firm-ly stood, And shall from age to age en-dure.
Praise Him a-bove, ye heaven-ly host; Praise Fa-ther, Son, and Ho-ly Ghost.

124 Come, Thou Almighty King

Anonymous ITALIAN HYMN FELICE DE GIARDINI

1. Come, Thou Al - might - y King, Help us Thy name to sing,
2. Come, Thou In - car - nate Word, Gird on Thy might - y sword,
3. Come, Ho - ly Com - fort - er, Thy sa - cred wit - ness bear
4. To the great One in Three E - ter - nal prais - es be

Help us to praise: Fa - ther, all - glo - ri - ous, O'er all vic-
Our prayer at - tend: Come, and Thy peo - ple bless, And give Thy
In this glad hour: Thou who al - might - y art, Now rule in
Hence ev - er - more. His sov-ereign maj - es - ty May we in

to - ri - ous, Come, and reign o - ver us, An - cient of Days.
Word suc - cess; Spir - it of ho - li - ness, On us de - scend.
ev - ery heart, And ne'er from us de - part, Spir - it of power.
glo - ry see, And to e - ter - ni - ty Love and a - dore.

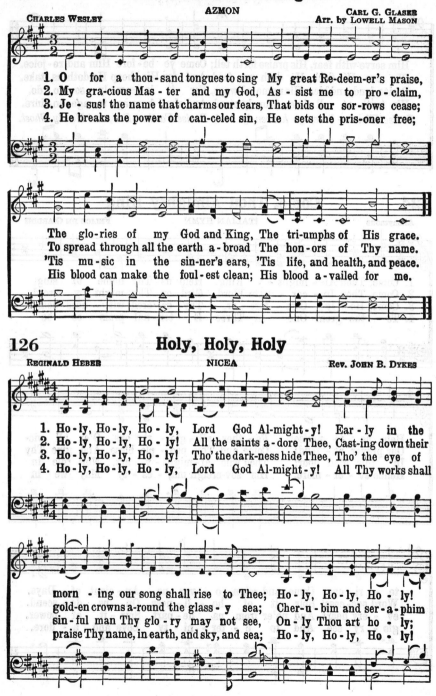

125

O For a Thousand Tongues

AZMON

CHARLES WESLEY

CARL G. GLASER
ARR. by LOWELL MASON

1. O for a thou-sand tongues to sing My great Re-deem-er's praise,
2. My gra-cious Mas-ter and my God, As-sist me to pro-claim,
3. Je-sus! the name that charms our fears, That bids our sor-rows cease;
4. He breaks the power of can-celed sin, He sets the pris-oner free;

The glo-ries of my God and King, The tri-umphs of His grace.
To spread through all the earth a-broad The hon-ors of Thy name.
'Tis mu-sic in the sin-ner's ears, 'Tis life, and health, and peace.
His blood can make the foul-est clean; His blood a-vailed for me.

126

Holy, Holy, Holy

NICEA

REGINALD HEBER

REV. JOHN B. DYKES

1. Ho-ly, Ho-ly, Ho-ly, Lord God Al-might-y! Ear-ly in the
2. Ho-ly, Ho-ly, Ho-ly! All the saints a-dore Thee, Cast-ing down their
3. Ho-ly, Ho-ly, Ho-ly! Tho' the dark-ness hide Thee, Tho' the eye of
4. Ho-ly, Ho-ly, Ho-ly, Lord God Al-might-y! All Thy works shall

morn-ing our song shall rise to Thee; Ho-ly, Ho-ly, Ho-ly!
gold-en crowns a-round the glass-y sea; Cher-u-bim and ser-a-phim
sin-ful man Thy glo-ry may not see, On-ly Thou art ho-ly;
praise Thy name, in earth, and sky, and sea; Ho-ly, Ho-ly, Ho-ly!

Holy, Holy, Holy

Mer - ci - ful and Might-y! God in Three per - sons, bless-ed Trin - i - ty!
fall-ing down be-fore Thee, Who wert, and art, and ev - er-more shalt be.
there is none be-side Thee Per - fect in power, in love, and pu - ri - ty.
Mer - ci - ful and Might-y! God in Three per - sons, bless-ed Trin - i - ty!

127 When Morning Gilds the Skies

LAUDES DOMINI

From the German
Tr. by EDWARD CASWALL

JOSEPH BARNBY

1. When morn-ing gilds the skies, My heart a - wak-ing cries:
2. Does sad-ness fill my mind, A sol - ace here I find:
3. In heaven's e - ter - nal bliss The love-liest strain is this,
4. Be this, while life is mine, My can - ti - cle di - vine,

May Je - sus Christ be praised! A - like at work and prayer
May Je - sus Christ be praised! Or fades my earth-ly bliss,
May Je - sus Christ be praised! The powers of dark-ness fear,
May Je - sus Christ be praised! Be this th' e - ter - nal song,

To Je - sus I re - pair: May Je - sus Christ be praised!
My com - fort still is this: May Je - sus Christ be praised!
When this sweet chant they hear: May Je - sus Christ be praised!
Through all the a - ges long: May Je - sus Christ be praised!

128 Safely Through Another Week

JOHN NEWTON   SABBATH   LOWELL MASON

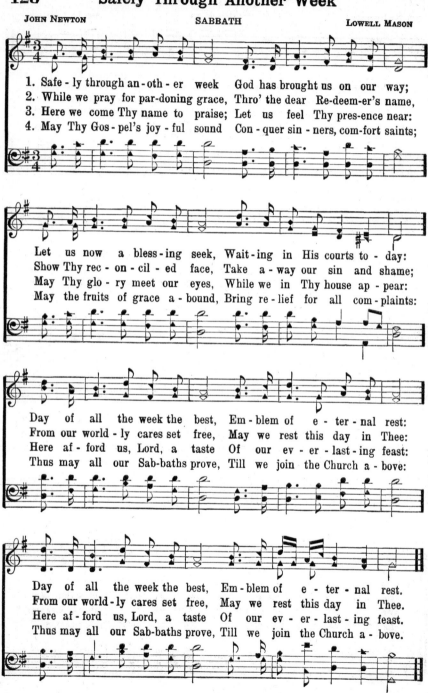

1. Safe - ly through an - oth - er week God has brought us on our way;
2. While we pray for par-doning grace, Thro' the dear Re-deem-er's name,
3. Here we come Thy name to praise; Let us feel Thy pres-ence near:
4. May Thy Gos-pel's joy - ful sound Con - quer sin - ners, com-fort saints;

Let us now a bless-ing seek, Wait-ing in His courts to - day:
Show Thy rec - on - cil - ed face, Take a - way our sin and shame;
May Thy glo - ry meet our eyes, While we in Thy house ap - pear:
May the fruits of grace a - bound, Bring re - lief for all com-plaints:

Day of all the week the best, Em - blem of e - ter - nal rest:
From our world - ly cares set free, May we rest this day in Thee:
Here af - ford us, Lord, a taste Of our ev - er - last-ing feast:
Thus may all our Sab-baths prove, Till we join the Church a - bove:

Day of all the week the best, Em - blem of e - ter - nal rest.
From our world - ly cares set free, May we rest this day in Thee.
Here af - ford us, Lord, a taste Of our ev - er - last - ing feast.
Thus may all our Sab-baths prove, Till we join the Church a - bove.

129   O Day of Rest and Gladness

C. WORDSWORTH   MENDEBRAS   ARR. by L. MASON

1. O day of rest and glad-ness, O day of joy and light,
2. On thee, at the cre-a-tion, The light first had its birth;
3. To-day on wea-ry na-tions The heaven-ly man-na falls;
4. New grac-es ev-er gain-ing From this our day of rest,

O balm of care and sad-ness, Most beau-ti-ful, most bright;
On thee, for our sal-va-tion, Christ rose from depths of earth;
To ho-ly con-vo-ca-tions The sil-ver trump-et calls,
We reach the rest re-main-ing To spir-its of the blest.

On thee, the high and low-ly, Bend-ing be-fore the throne,
On thee, our Lord, vic-to-rious, The Spir-it sent from heaven;
Where Gos-pel light is glow-ing With pure and ra-diant beams,
To Ho-ly Ghost be prais-es, To Fa-ther, and to Son;

Sing "Ho-ly, Ho-ly, Ho-ly," To the great Three in One.
And thus on thee, most glo-rious, A tri-ple light was given.
And liv-ing wa-ter flow-ing With soul-re-fresh-ing streams.
The Church her voice up-rais-es To Thee, blest Three in One.

130 Day Is Dying in the West

Mary A. Lathbury

William F. Sherwin

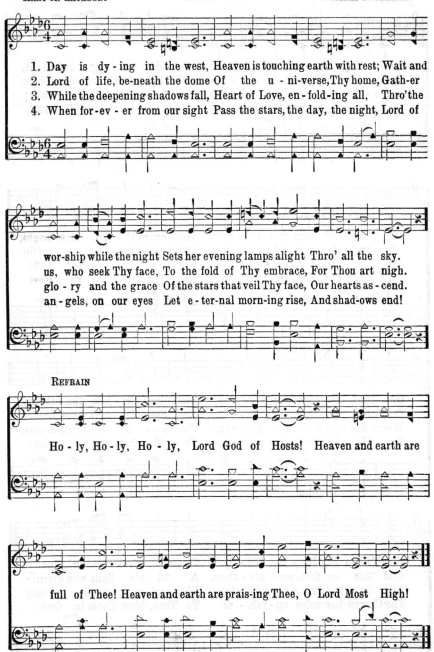

1. Day is dy-ing in the west, Heaven is touching earth with rest; Wait and
2. Lord of life, be-neath the dome Of the u - ni-verse, Thy home, Gath-er
3. While the deepening shadows fall, Heart of Love, en-fold-ing all, Thro' the
4. When for-ev - er from our sight Pass the stars, the day, the night, Lord of

wor-ship while the night Sets her evening lamps alight Thro' all the sky.
us, who seek Thy face, To the fold of Thy embrace, For Thou art nigh.
glo - ry and the grace Of the stars that veil Thy face, Our hearts as - cend.
an - gels, on our eyes Let e - ter-nal morn-ing rise, And shad-ows end!

REFRAIN

Ho - ly, Ho - ly, Ho - ly, Lord God of Hosts! Heaven and earth are

full of Thee! Heaven and earth are prais-ing Thee, O Lord Most High!

Higher Ground

Johnson Oatman, Jr. Chas. H. Gabriel.

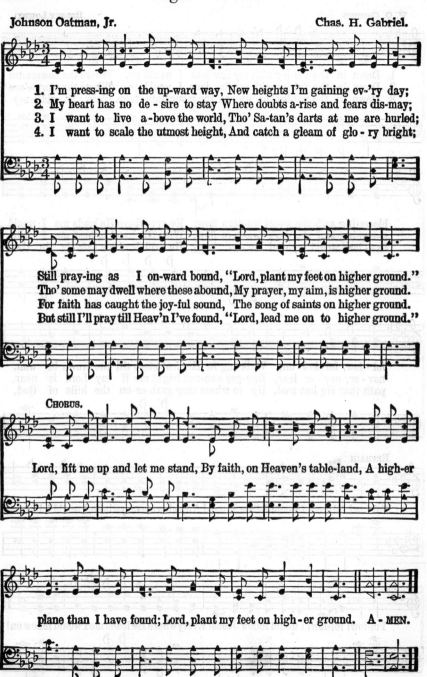

1. I'm press-ing on the up-ward way, New heights I'm gaining ev-'ry day;
2. My heart has no de-sire to stay Where doubts a-rise and fears dis-may;
3. I want to live a-bove the world, Tho' Sa-tan's darts at me are hurled;
4. I want to scale the utmost height, And catch a gleam of glo-ry bright;

Still pray-ing as I on-ward bound, "Lord, plant my feet on higher ground."
Tho' some may dwell where these abound, My prayer, my aim, is higher ground.
For faith has caught the joy-ful sound, The song of saints on higher ground.
But still I'll pray till Heav'n I've found, "Lord, lead me on to higher ground."

Chorus.

Lord, lift me up and let me stand, By faith, on Heaven's table-land, A high-er
plane than I have found; Lord, plant my feet on high-er ground. A - men.

Follow On

W. O. CUSHING

ROBERT LOWRY

1. Down in the val-ley with my Sav-iour I would go, Where the flowers are
2. Down in the val-ley with my Sav-iour I would go, Where the storms are
3. Down in the val-ley, or up-on the moun-tain steep, Close be-side my

bloom-ing and the sweet wa-ters flow; Ev-ery-where He leads me I would
sweep-ing and the dark wa-ters flow; With His hand to lead me I will
Sav-iour would my soul ev-er keep; He will lead me safe-ly in the

fol-low, fol-low on, Walk-ing in His foot-steps till the crown be won.
nev-er, nev-er fear, Dan-ger can-not fright me if my Lord is near.
path that He has trod, Up to where they gath-er on the hills of God.

REFRAIN

Fol-low! fol-low! I would follow Je-sus! Anywhere, everywhere, I would follow on!

Fol-low! fol-low! I would follow Jesus! Everywhere He leads me I would follow on!

133 The Never-Failing Hand

B. B. McK.

B. B. McKinney

1. When my bark is cast in a storm-y blast, And I'm driv-en a-
2. Though the bil-lows roll o'er my trou-bled soul, I will fol-low His
3. When the storms are o'er, gone for-ev-er-more, And I come to the

far from land; I will look to Christ who will hold me fast With His
wise com-mand; I will trust my all to His blest con-trol, For I'm
morn-ing-land, I will walk with Him on the gold-en shore, For He

Chorus

nev-er, nev-er fail-ing hand.
an-chored in His might-y hand. He will hold me, He will hold me,
holds me with His might-y hand.

On the ev-er-last-ing Rock I stand; I stand; Wheth-er wak-ing,

wheth-er sleep-ing, "He will hold me with His might-y hand."

134 When the Morning Comes

Words Adapted
Southern Melody
Arr. by B. B. McKinney

Slowly

1. Tri - als dark on ev - ery hand, And we can-not un - der-stand All the ways that
2. Oft our cherished plans have failed, Disappointments have prevailed, And we've wandered
3. Temp-ta-tions, hid-den snares, Of-ten take us un - a - wares, And our hearts are

God would lead us to that bless-ed promised land; But He'll guide us with His eye,
in the darkness, heav-y-heart-ed and a - lone; But we're trusting in the Lord,
made to bleed for some tho't-less word or deed, And we won-der why the test

And we'll fol-low till we die; We will un-der-stand it bet-ter by and by.
And, ac-cord-ing to His word, We will un-der-stand it bet-ter by and by.
When we try to do our best, But we'll un-der-stand it bet-ter by and by.

CHORUS

By and by, when the morning comes, When the saints of God are gathered home, We will

tell the sto - ry How we've overcome; We will un-der-stand it bet-ter by and by.

135   The Beautiful Garden of Prayer

ELEANOR ALLEN SCHROLL   J. H. FILLMORE

1. There's a gar-den where Je-sus is wait-ing, There's a place that is
2. There's a gar-den where Je-sus is wait-ing, And I go with my
3. There's a gar-den where Je-sus is wait-ing, And He bids you to

won-drous-ly fair; For it glows with the light of His pres-ence, 'Tis the
bur-den and care, Just to learn from His lips words of com-fort, In the
come meet Him there, Just to walk and to talk with my Sav-iour, In the

REFRAIN

beau-ti-ful gar-den of prayer. O the beau-ti-ful gar-den, the

gar-den of prayer, O the beau-ti-ful gar-den of prayer; There my Sav-iour a-

poco rit. - - - - - -

waits, and He o-pens the gates To the beau-ti-ful gar-den of prayer.

His Way with Thee

C. S. N.

CYRUS S. NUSBAUM

1. Would you live for Je-sus, and be al-ways pure and good? Would you walk with
2. Would you have Him make you free, and fol-low at His call? Would you know the
3. Would you in His king-dom find a place of con-stant rest? Would you prove Him

Him with-in the nar-row road? Would you have Him bear your bur-den, car-ry
peace that comes by giv-ing all? Would you have Him save you, so that you can
true in prov-i-den-tial test? Would you in His serv-ice la-bor al-ways

Chorus

all your load? Let Him have His way with thee.
nev-er fall? Let Him have His way with thee. His power can make you what you
at your best? Let Him have His way with thee.

ought to be; His blood can cleanse your heart and make you free; His love can

rit.

fill your soul, and you will see 'Twas best for Him to have His way with thee.

137   Serve the Lord with Gladness

B. B. McK.

B. B. McKinney

1. "Serve the Lord with gladness" In our works and ways, Come be-fore His pres-ence
2. "Serve the Lord with gladness," Thankful all the while For His ten-der mer-cies,
3. "Serve the Lord with gladness," This shall be our theme, As we walk to-geth-er

With our songs of praise; Un - to Him our Mak-er We would pledge anew (a-new),
For His lov - ing smile. Bless-ed truth en-dur - ing, Always just the same (the same),
In His love su - preme. Listening, ev - er lis-tening, For the still small voice (His voice),

Chorus

Life's supreme de-vo-tion To serv-ice true.
We will serve with gladness And praise His name. "Serve Him with gladness," Enter His courts with
His sweet will so precious Will be our choice.

song (with song); To our Cre - a - tor True praises be-long (belong). Great is His mer-cy,

rit.

Won-der-ful is His name (His name), We glad-ly serve Him, His great love proclaim (proclaim).

138 "Whosoever Will"

P. P. B.

P. P. Bliss

1. "Who-so-ev-er hear-eth," shout, shout the sound! Spread the bless-ed ti-dings
2. Who-so-ev-er com-eth need not de-lay, Now the door is o-pen,
3. "Who-so-ev-er will!" the prom-ise is se-cure; "Who-so-ev-er will," for-

all the world a-round; Tell the joy-ful news wher-ev-er man is found,
en-ter while you may; Je-sus is the true, the on-ly Liv-ing Way:
ev-er must en-dure; "Who-so-ev-er will!" 'tis life for-ev-er-more;

CHORUS

"Who-so-ev-er will may come." "Who-so-ev-er will, who-so-ev-er will!"

Send the proc-la-ma-tion o-ver vale and hill; 'Tis a lov-ing

Fa-ther calls the wan-derer home: "Who-so-ev-er will may come."

Christic Arose

139 Christ Arose

ROBERT LOWRY

ROBERT LOWRY

1. Low in the grave He lay— Je - sus my Sav - iour! Wait-ing the com-ing day—
2. Vain-ly they watch His bed— Je - sus my Sav - iour! Vain-ly they seal the dead—
3. Death cannot keep his prey— Je - sus my Sav - iour! He tore the bars a - way—

REFRAIN *Faster*

Je - sus my Lord! Up from the grave He a - rose (He a-rose), With a

might-y tri-umph o'er His foes; (He a-rose!) He a - rose a Vic-tor from the

dark do - main, And He lives for - ev - er with His saints to reign. He a-

rit.

rose! He a - rose! Hal - le - lu - jah! Christ a - rose!

He a-rose! He a-rose!

Joy to the World!

ANTIOCH

Isaac Watts

George F. Handel

1. Joy to the world! the Lord is come; Let earth re-
2. Joy to the earth! the Sav-iour reigns; Let men their
3. No more let sins and sor-rows grow, Nor thorns in-
4. He rules the world with truth and grace, And makes the

ceive her King; Let ev-ery heart pre-pare Him room,
songs em-ploy; While fields and floods, rocks, hills and plains
fest the ground; He comes to make His bless-ings flow
na-tions prove The glo-ries of His right-eous-ness,

And heaven and na-ture sing,   And heaven and na-ture
Re-peat the sound-ing joy,   Re-peat the sound-ing
Far as the curse is found,   Far as the curse is
And won-ders of His love,   And won-ders of His

1. And heaven and na-ture sing,........... And

sing,   And heaven, and heaven and na-ture sing.
joy,   Re-peat, re-peat the sound-ing joy.
found,   Far as, far as the curse is found.
love,   And won-ders, and won-ders of His love.

heaven and na-ture sing,

141   It Came Upon the Midnight Clear

CAROL

Edmund H. Sears   Richard S. Willis

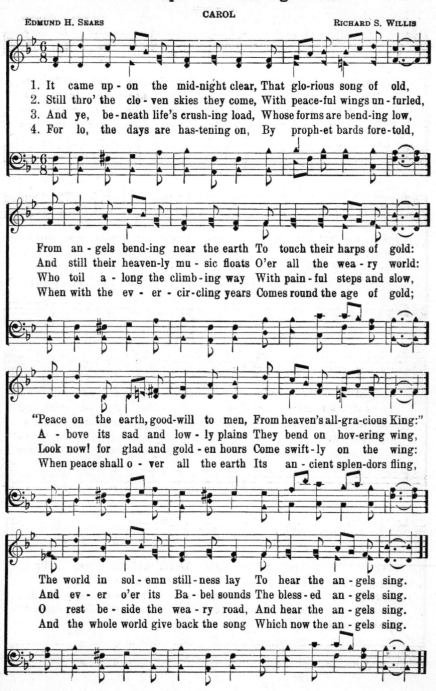

1. It came up-on the mid-night clear, That glo-rious song of old,
2. Still thro' the clo-ven skies they come, With peace-ful wings un-furled,
3. And ye, be-neath life's crush-ing load, Whose forms are bend-ing low,
4. For lo, the days are has-tening on, By proph-et bards fore-told,

From an-gels bend-ing near the earth To touch their harps of gold:
And still their heaven-ly mu-sic floats O'er all the wea-ry world:
Who toil a-long the climb-ing way With pain-ful steps and slow,
When with the ev-er-cir-cling years Comes round the age of gold;

"Peace on the earth, good-will to men, From heaven's all-gra-cious King:"
A-bove its sad and low-ly plains They bend on hov-ering wing,
Look now! for glad and gold-en hours Come swift-ly on the wing:
When peace shall o-ver all the earth Its an-cient splen-dors fling,

The world in sol-emn still-ness lay To hear the an-gels sing.
And ev-er o'er its Ba-bel sounds The bless-ed an-gels sing.
O rest be-side the wea-ry road, And hear the an-gels sing.
And the whole world give back the song Which now the an-gels sing.

Hark, the Herald Angels Sing

MENDELSSOHN

CHARLES WESLEY   FELIX MENDELSSOHN

1. Hark! the her-ald an-gels sing, "Glo-ry to the new-born King;
2. Christ, by high-est heaven a-dored; Christ, the ev-er-last-ing Lord:
3. Hail the heaven-born Prince of Peace! Hail the Sun of right-eous-ness!
4. Come, De-sire of na-tions, come! Fix in us Thy hum-ble home:

Peace on earth, and mer-cy mild; God and sin-ners rec-on-ciled."
Late in time be-hold Him come, Off-spring of a vir-gin's womb.
Light and life to all He brings, Risen with heal-ing in His wings:
Rise, the wom-an's conquering seed, Bruise in us the ser-pent's head;

Joy-ful, all ye na-tions, rise, Join the tri-umph of the skies;
Veiled in flesh the God-head see, Hail th' in-car-nate De-i-ty!
Mild He lays His glo-ry by, Born that man no more may die;
Ad-am's like-ness now ef-face, Stamp Thine im-age in its place:

With th' an-gel-ic hosts pro-claim, "Christ is born in Beth-le-hem."
Pleased as man with men t' ap-pear, Je-sus our Im-man-uel here.
Born to raise the sons of earth; Born to give them sec-ond birth.
Sec-ond Ad-am from a-bove, Re-in-state us in Thy love.

Hark! the Herald Angels Sing

Hark! the her-ald an-gels sing, "Glo-ry to the new-born King."

143 **O Come, All Ye Faithful**

Tr. by FREDERICK OAKELEY   ADESTE FIDELES   WADE'S Cantus Diversi

1. O come, all ye faith-ful, joy-ful and tri-um-phant, O
2. Sing, choirs of an-gels, sing in ex-ul-ta-tion, O
3. Yea, Lord, we greet Thee, born this hap-py morn-ing,

come ye, O come ye to Beth-le-hem; Come and be-hold Him
sing, all ye bright hosts of heaven a-bove; Glo-ry to God, all
Je-sus, to Thee be all glo-ry given; Word of the Fa-ther,

REFRAIN

born the King of an-gels;
glo-ry in the high-est; O come, let us a-dore Him, O
now in flesh ap-pear-ing;

come, let us a-dore Him, O come, let us a-dore Him, Christ, the Lord.

144 O Little Town of Bethlehem

PHILLIPS BROOKS   ST. LOUIS   LEWIS H. REDNER

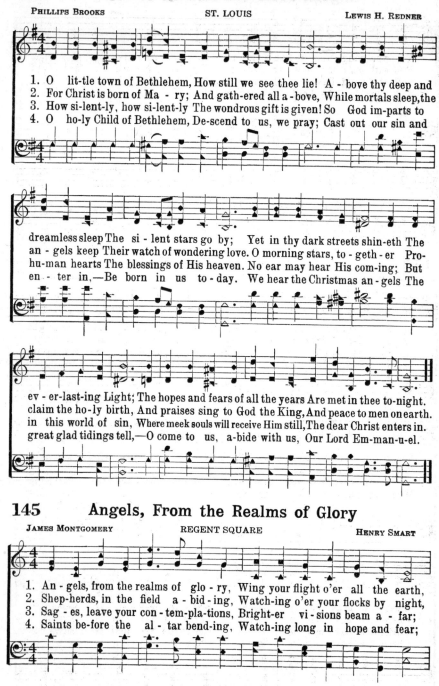

1. O lit-tle town of Bethlehem, How still we see thee lie! A - bove thy deep and dreamless sleep The si - lent stars go by; Yet in thy dark streets shin-eth The ev - er-last-ing Light; The hopes and fears of all the years Are met in thee to-night.

2. For Christ is born of Ma - ry; And gath-ered all a-bove, While mortals sleep, the an - gels keep Their watch of wondering love. O morning stars, to - geth - er Pro-claim the ho-ly birth, And praises sing to God the King, And peace to men on earth.

3. How si-lent-ly, how si-lent-ly The wondrous gift is given! So God im-parts to hu-man hearts The blessings of His heaven. No ear may hear His com-ing; But in this world of sin, Where meek souls will receive Him still, The dear Christ enters in.

4. O ho-ly Child of Bethlehem, De-scend to us, we pray; Cast out our sin and en - ter in,—Be born in us to - day. We hear the Christmas an - gels The great glad tidings tell,—O come to us, a-bide with us, Our Lord Em-man-u-el.

145 Angels, From the Realms of Glory

JAMES MONTGOMERY   REGENT SQUARE   HENRY SMART

1. An - gels, from the realms of glo - ry, Wing your flight o'er all the earth,
2. Shep-herds, in the field a - bid - ing, Watch-ing o'er your flocks by night,
3. Sag - es, leave your con - tem-pla-tions, Bright-er vi - sions beam a - far;
4. Saints be-fore the al - tar bend-ing, Watch-ing long in hope and fear;

Angels, From the Realms of Glory

Ye, who sang cre - a - tion's sto - ry, Now pro-claim Mes - si - ah's birth:
God with man is now re - sid - ing, Yon-der shines the In - fant-Light;
Seek the great De - sire of na - tions, Ye have seen His na - tal star;
Sud - den - ly the Lord, de-scend-ing, In His tem - ple shall ap - pear;

Come and wor-ship, come and wor-ship, Wor - ship Christ, the new-born King.

146 Silent Night, Holy Night

JOSEPH MOHR   STILLE NACHT   FRANZ GRÜBER

1. Si - lent night, ho - ly night, All is calm, all is bright
2. Si - lent night, ho - ly night, Dark-ness flies, all is light;
3. Si - lent night, ho - ly night, Guid - ing Star, lend thy light;
4. Si - lent night, ho - ly night, Wondrous Star, lend thy light;

Round yon Vir - gin Moth-er and Child, Ho - ly In-fant so ten-der and mild,
Shep-herds hear the an - gels sing, "Al - le - lu - ia! hail the King!
See the east-ern wise men bring Gifts and hom - age to our King!
With the an - gels let us sing Al - le - lu - ia to our King!

Sleep in heav - en - ly peace, Sleep in heav - en - ly peace.
Christ the Sav - iour is born, Christ the Sav - iour is born."
Christ the Sav - iour is born, Christ the Sav - iour is born.
Christ the Sav - iour is born, Christ the Sav - iour is born.

147 While Shepherds Watched Their Flocks

NAHUM TATE   CHRISTMAS   GEORGE F. HÄNDEL

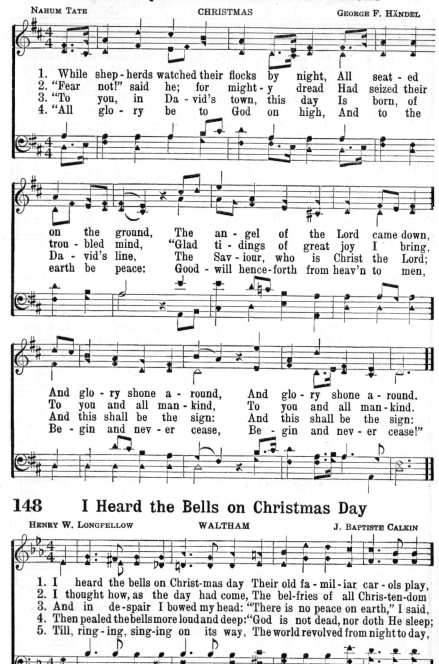

1. While shep-herds watched their flocks by night, All seat-ed
2. "Fear not!" said he; for might-y dread Had seized their
3. "To you, in Da-vid's town, this day Is born, of
4. "All glo-ry be to God on high, And to the

on the ground, The an-gel of the Lord came down,
trou-bled mind, "Glad ti-dings of great joy I bring,
Da-vid's line, The Sav-iour, who is Christ the Lord;
earth be peace: Good-will hence-forth from heav'n to men,

And glo-ry shone a-round, And glo-ry shone a-round.
To you and all man-kind, To you and all man-kind.
And this shall be the sign: And this shall be the sign:
Be-gin and nev-er cease, Be-gin and nev-er cease!"

148 I Heard the Bells on Christmas Day

HENRY W. LONGFELLOW   WALTHAM   J. BAPTISTE CALKIN

1. I heard the bells on Christ-mas day Their old fa-mil-iar car-ols play,
2. I thought how, as the day had come, The bel-fries of all Chris-ten-dom
3. And in de-spair I bowed my head: "There is no peace on earth," I said,
4. Then pealed the bells more loud and deep: "God is not dead, nor doth He sleep;
5. Till, ring-ing, sing-ing on its way, The world revolved from night to day,

I Heard the Bells on Christmas Day

And wild and sweet the words re-peat Of peace on earth, good-will to men.
Had rolled a-long th' un-bro-ken song Of peace on earth, good-will to men.
"For hate is strong, and mocks the song Of peace on earth, good-will to men."
The wrong shall fail, the right pre-vail, With peace on earth, good-will to men:"
A voice, a chime, a chant sub-lime, Of peace on earth, good-will to men!

149 Something For Jesus

S. D. PHELPS

ROBERT LOWRY

1. Sav - iour, Thy dy - ing love Thou gav - est me, Nor should I
2. At the blest mer - cy - seat, Plead - ing for me, My fee - ble
3. Give me a faith - ful heart,—Like - ness to Thee,— That each de -
4. All that I am and have,—Thy gifts so free,— In joy, in

aught with-hold, Dear Lord, from Thee: In love my soul would bow,
faith looks up, Je - sus, to Thee: Help me the cross to bear,
part - ing day Hence-forth may see Some work of love be - gun,
grief, thro' life, Dear Lord, for Thee! And when Thy face I see,

My heart ful - fill its vow, Some offering bring Thee now, Something for Thee.
Thy won-drous love de-clare, Some song to raise, or prayer, Something for Thee.
Some deed of kind-ness done, Some wanderer sought and won, Something for Thee.
My ran-somed soul shall be, Thro' all e - ter - ni - ty, Something for Thee.

150 Jesus Shall Reign

ISAAC WATTS   DUKE STREET   JOHN HATTON

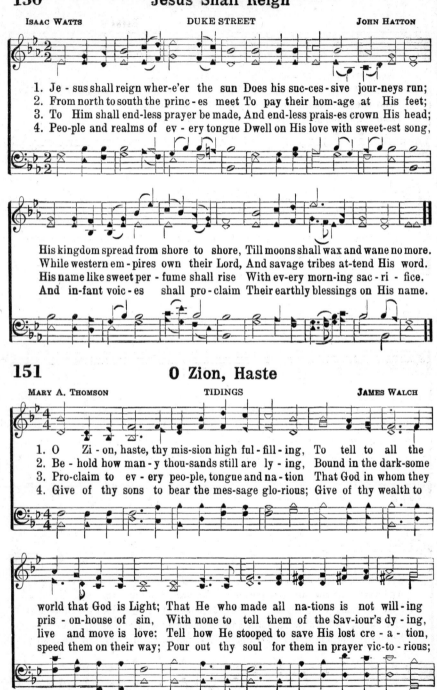

1. Je - sus shall reign wher-e'er the sun Does his suc-ces-sive jour-neys run;
2. From north to south the princ - es meet To pay their hom-age at His feet;
3. To Him shall end-less prayer be made, And end-less prais-es crown His head;
4. Peo-ple and realms of ev - ery tongue Dwell on His love with sweet-est song,

His kingdom spread from shore to shore, Till moons shall wax and wane no more.
While western em - pires own their Lord, And savage tribes at-tend His word.
His name like sweet per - fume shall rise With ev-ery morn-ing sac - ri - fice.
And in-fant voic - es shall pro - claim Their earthly blessings on His name.

151 O Zion, Haste

MARY A. THOMSON   TIDINGS   JAMES WALCH

1. O Zi - on, haste, thy mis-sion high ful - fill - ing, To tell to all the
2. Be - hold how man - y thou-sands still are ly - ing, Bound in the dark-some
3. Pro-claim to ev - ery peo-ple, tongue and na - tion That God in whom they
4. Give of thy sons to bear the mes-sage glo-rious; Give of thy wealth to

world that God is Light; That He who made all na-tions is not will-ing
pris - on-house of sin, With none to tell them of the Sav-iour's dy - ing,
live and move is love: Tell how He stooped to save His lost cre - a - tion,
speed them on their way; Pour out thy soul for them in prayer vic-to - rious;

O Zion, Haste

One soul should per-ish, lost in shades of night.
Or of the life He died for them to win. Pub-lish glad ti-dings,
And died on earth that man might live a-bove.
And all thou spend-est Je-sus will re-pay.

REFRAIN

Ti-dings of peace; Ti-dings of Je-sus, Re-demp-tion and re-lease.

152   Fling Out the Banner! Let It Float

GEORGE W. DOANE   DOANE   J. BAPTISTE CALKIN

1. Fling out the ban-ner! let it float Sky-ward and sea-ward, high and wide;
2. Fling out the ban-ner! an-gels bend In anx-ious si-lence o'er the sign,
3. Fling out the ban-ner! hea-then lands Shall see from far the glo-rious sight,
4. Fling out the ban-ner! sin-sick souls, That sink and per-ish in the strife,
5. Fling out the ban-ner! wide and high, Sea-ward and sky-ward, let it shine:

The sun that lights its shin-ing folds, The cross on which the Sav-iour died.
And vain-ly seek to com-pre-hend The won-der of the love di-vine.
And na-tions crowd-ing to be born, Bap-tize their spir-its in its light.
Shall touch in faith its ra-diant hem, And spring im-mor-tal in-to life.
Nor skill, nor might, nor mer-it ours; We con-quer on-ly in that sign.

153 I Love Him

English Hymn Book

S. C. Foster

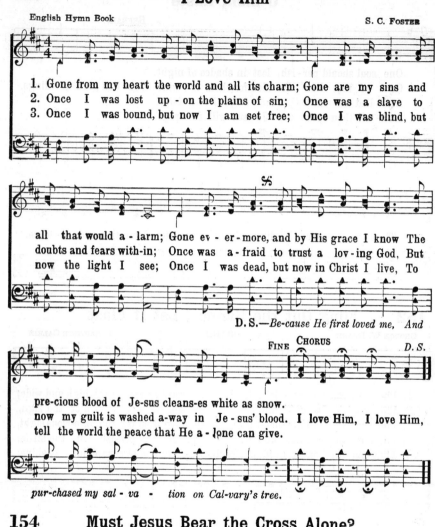

1. Gone from my heart the world and all its charm; Gone are my sins and
2. Once I was lost up - on the plains of sin; Once was a slave to
3. Once I was bound, but now I am set free; Once I was blind, but

all that would a - larm; Gone ev - er - more, and by His grace I know The
doubts and fears with-in; Once was a-fraid to trust a lov-ing God, But
now the light I see; Once I was dead, but now in Christ I live, To

D.S.—*Be-cause He first loved me, And*

FINE **CHORUS** D.S.

pre-cious blood of Je-sus cleans-es white as snow.
now my guilt is washed a-way in Je-sus' blood. I love Him, I love Him,
tell the world the peace that He a - lone can give.

pur-chased my sal - va - tion on Cal-vary's tree.

154 Must Jesus Bear the Cross Alone?

THOMAS SHEPHERD MAITLAND GEORGE N. ALLEN

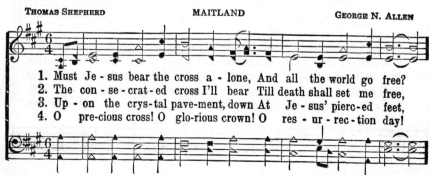

1. Must Je - sus bear the cross a - lone, And all the world go free?
2. The con - se - crat - ed cross I'll bear Till death shall set me free,
3. Up - on the crys - tal pave-ment, down At Je - sus' pierc-ed feet,
4. O pre-cious cross! O glo-rious crown! O res - ur - rec - tion day!

Must Jesus Bear the Cross Alone?

No; there's a cross for ev-ery one, And there's a cross for me.
And then go home my crown to wear, For there's a crown for me.
Joy-ful, I'll cast my gold-en crown, And His dear name re-peat.
Ye an-gels, from the stars come down, And bear my soul a-way.

155 Glory to His Name

Rev. E. A. HOFFMAN

Rev. J. H. STOCKTON

1. Down at the cross where my Sav-iour died, Down where for cleansing from
2. I am so won-drous-ly saved from sin, Je-sus so sweet-ly a-
3. Oh, pre-cious foun-tain that saves from sin, I am so glad I have
4. Come to this foun-tain so rich and sweet; Cast thy poor soul at the

FINE

sin I cried, There to my heart was the blood ap-plied; Glo-ry to His name.
bides with-in, There at the cross where He took me in; Glo-ry to His name.
en-tered in; There Je-sus saves me and keeps me clean; Glo-ry to His name.
Sav-iour's feet; Plunge in to-day, and be made com-plete; Glo-ry to His name.

D. S.—*There to my heart was the blood ap-plied; Glo-ry to His name.*

CHORUS

D. S.

Glo-ry to His name,.. Glo-ry to His name;..

156 **Near the Cross**

FANNY J. CROSBY

W. H. DOANE

1. Je - sus, keep me near the cross, There a pre - cious foun - tain
2. Near the cross, a trem-bling soul, Love and mer - cy found me;
3. Near the cross! O Lamb of God, Bring its scenes be - fore me;
4. Near the cross I'll watch and wait, Hop - ing, trust - ing ev - er,

Free to all— a heal-ing stream, Flows from Cal-v'ry's moun - tain.
There the Bright and Morn-ing Star Sheds its beams a - round me.
Help me walk from day to day, With its shad - ows o'er me.
Till I reach the gold - en strand, Just be - yond the riv - er.

CHORUS

In the cross, in the cross, Be my glo - ry ev - er;

Till my rap - tured soul shall find Rest be - yond the riv - er.

157 **'Tis Midnight**

WILLIAM B. TAPPAN

OLIVE'S BROW

WILLIAM B. BRADBURY

1. 'Tis midnight; and on Ol - ive's brow The star is dimmed that late-ly shone:
2. 'Tis midnight; and from all removed, The Sav-iour wrestles lone with fears;
3. 'Tis midnight; and for oth - ers' guilt The Man of Sor-rows weeps in blood;
4. 'Tis midnight; and from ether-plains Is borne the song that an - gels know;

'Tis Midnight

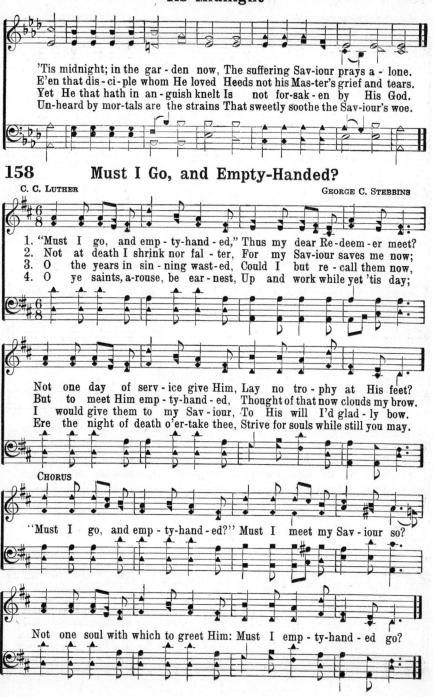

'Tis midnight; in the gar-den now, The suffering Sav-iour prays a-lone.
E'en that dis-ci-ple whom He loved Heeds not his Mas-ter's grief and tears.
Yet He that hath in an-guish knelt Is not for-sak-en by His God.
Un-heard by mor-tals are the strains That sweetly soothe the Sav-iour's woe.

158 Must I Go, and Empty-Handed?

C. C. LUTHER

GEORGE C. STEBBINS

1. "Must I go, and emp-ty-hand-ed," Thus my dear Re-deem-er meet?
2. Not at death I shrink nor fal-ter, For my Sav-iour saves me now;
3. O the years in sin-ning wast-ed, Could I but re-call them now,
4. O ye saints, a-rouse, be ear-nest, Up and work while yet 'tis day;

Not one day of serv-ice give Him, Lay no tro-phy at His feet?
But to meet Him emp-ty-hand-ed, Thought of that now clouds my brow.
I would give them to my Sav-iour, To His will I'd glad-ly bow.
Ere the night of death o'er-take thee, Strive for souls while still you may.

CHORUS

"Must I go, and emp-ty-hand-ed?" Must I meet my Sav-iour so?

Not one soul with which to greet Him: Must I emp-ty-hand-ed go?

159 **Jesus Calls Us**

Mrs. Cecil F. Alexander   GALILEE   William H. Jude

1. Je - sus calls us; o'er the tu - mult Of our life's wild, rest-less sea,
2. Je - sus calls us from the wor - ship Of the vain world's gold-en store,
3. In our joys and in our sor - rows, Days of toil and hours of ease,
4. Je - sus calls us: by Thy mer - cies, Sav-iour, may we hear Thy call,

Day by day His sweet voice sound-eth, Say-ing, "Chris-tian, fol - low Me."
From each i - dol that would keep us, Say-ing, "Chris-tian, love Me more."
Still He calls, in cares and pleas-ures, "Chris-tian, love Me more than these."
Give our hearts to Thy o - be-dience, Serve and love Thee best of all.

160 **What a Friend**

Joseph Scriven   CONVERSE   Charles C. Converse

1. What a Friend we have in Je - sus, All our sins and griefs to bear!
2. Have we tri - als and temp-ta - tions? Is there trou-ble an - y - where?
3. Are we weak and heav-y - la - den, Cum-bered with a load of care?—

What a priv - i - lege to car - ry Ev - ery-thing to God in prayer!
We should nev - er be dis - cour-aged, Take it to the Lord in prayer.
Pre - cious Sav-iour, still our ref - uge,— Take it to the Lord in prayer.

What a Friend

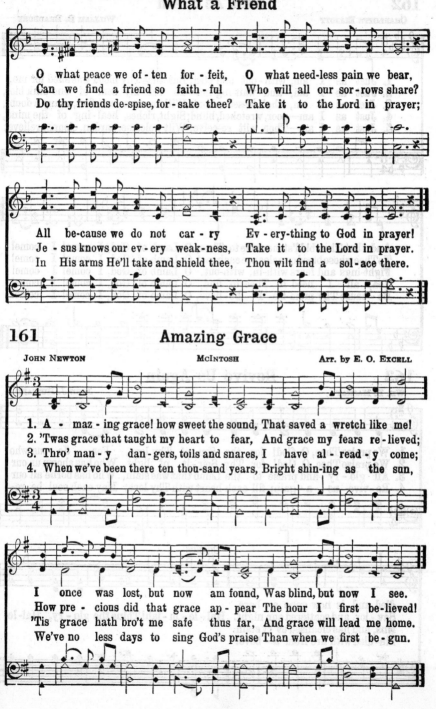

O what peace we of-ten for-feit, O what need-less pain we bear,
Can we find a friend so faith-ful Who will all our sor-rows share?
Do thy friends de-spise, for-sake thee? Take it to the Lord in prayer;

All be-cause we do not car-ry Ev-ery-thing to God in prayer!
Je-sus knows our ev-ery weak-ness, Take it to the Lord in prayer.
In His arms He'll take and shield thee, Thou wilt find a sol-ace there.

161 Amazing Grace

JOHN NEWTON   MCINTOSH   ARR. by E. O. EXCELL

1. A - maz - ing grace! how sweet the sound, That saved a wretch like me!
2. 'Twas grace that taught my heart to fear, And grace my fears re-lieved;
3. Thro' man - y dan - gers, toils and snares, I have al-read-y come;
4. When we've been there ten thou-sand years, Bright shin-ing as the sun,

I once was lost, but now am found, Was blind, but now I see.
How pre - cious did that grace ap - pear The hour I first be-lieved!
'Tis grace hath bro't me safe thus far, And grace will lead me home.
We've no less days to sing God's praise Than when we first be-gun.

162 Just As I Am

CHARLOTTE ELLIOTT

WILLIAM B. BRADBURY

1. Just as I am, with-out one plea, But that Thy blood was shed for me,
2. Just as I am, and wait-ing not To rid my soul of one dark blot,
3. Just as I am, tho' tossed a-bout With many a con-flict, many a doubt,
4. Just as I am—poor, wretched, blind; Sight, riches, heal-ing of the mind,
5. Just as I am—Thou wilt re-ceive, Wilt welcome, pardon, cleanse relieve;

And that Thou bidd'st me come to Thee, O Lamb of God, I come! I come!
To Thee whose blood can cleanse each spot, O Lamb of God, I come! I come!
Fight-ings and fears with-in, with-out, O Lamb of God, I come! I come!
Yea, all I need in Thee to find, O Lamb of God, I come! I come!
Be-cause Thy prom-ise I be-lieve, O Lamb of God, I come! I come!

163 Revive Us Again

WM. P. MACKAY

JOHN J. HUSBAND

1. We praise Thee, O God! for the Son of Thy love, For Je-sus who
2. We praise Thee, O God! for Thy Spir-it of light, Who has shown us our
3. All glo-ry and praise to the Lamb that was slain, Who has borne all our
4. Re-vive us a-gain; fill each heart with Thy love; May each soul be re-

CHORUS

died, and is now gone a-bove.
Sav-ior, and scattered our night. Hal-le-lu-jah! Thine the glo-ry, Hal-le-
sins, and has cleansed ev'ry stain.
kin-dled with fire from a-bove.

Revive Us Again

lu - jah! A - men; Hal - le - lu - jah! Thine the glo - ry, re - vive us a - gain.

164   Ready

S. E. L.   CHARLIE D. TILLMAN

1. Read-y to suf-fer grief or pain, Read-y to stand the test;
2. Read-y to go, read-y to bear, Read-y to watch and pray;
3. Read-y to speak, read-y to think, Read-y with heart and brain;
4. Read-y to speak, read-y to warn, Read-y o'er souls to yearn;

Read-y to stay at home and send Oth-ers, if He sees best.
Read-y to stand a - side and give, Till He shall clear the way.
Read-y to stand where He sees fit, Read-y to stand the strain.
Read-y in life, read-y in death, Read-y for His re - turn.

CHORUS.

Read-y to go, read-y to stay, Read-y my place to fill;

Read-y for serv-ice, low-ly or great, Read-y to do His will.

165

He Leadeth Me

JOSEPH H. GILMORE

WILLIAM B. BRADBURY

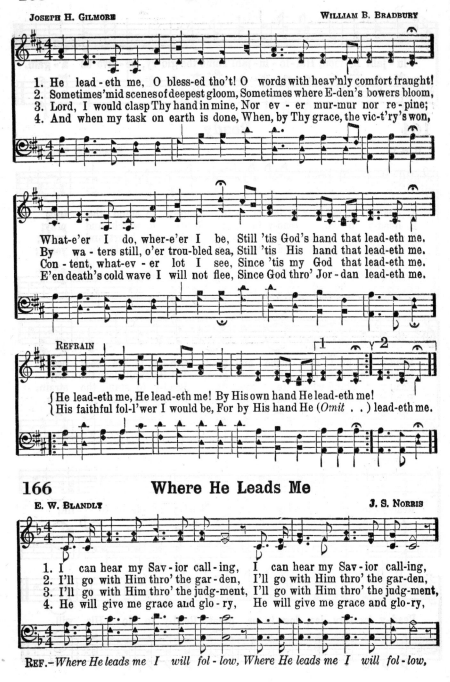

1. He lead - eth me, O bless - ed tho't! O words with heav'nly comfort fraught!
2. Sometimes 'mid scenes of deepest gloom, Sometimes where E-den's bowers bloom,
3. Lord, I would clasp Thy hand in mine, Nor ev - er mur-mur nor re - pine;
4. And when my task on earth is done, When, by Thy grace, the vic-t'ry's won,

What-e'er I do, wher-e'er I be, Still 'tis God's hand that lead-eth me.
By wa - ters still, o'er trou-bled sea, Still 'tis His hand that lead-eth me.
Con - tent, what-ev - er lot I see, Since 'tis my God that lead-eth me.
E'en death's cold wave I will not flee, Since God thro' Jor - dan lead-eth me.

REFRAIN

He lead-eth me, He lead-eth me! By His own hand He lead-eth me!
His faithful fol-l'wer I would be, For by His hand He (*Omit* . .) lead-eth me.

166

Where He Leads Me

E. W. BLANDLY

J. S. NORRIS

1. I can hear my Sav - ior call-ing, I can hear my Sav - ior call-ing,
2. I'll go with Him thro' the gar - den, I'll go with Him thro' the gar-den,
3. I'll go with Him thro' the judg-ment, I'll go with Him thro' the judg-ment,
4. He will give me grace and glo - ry, He will give me grace and glo-ry,

REF.—*Where He leads me I will fol - low, Where He leads me I will fol - low,*

Where He Leads Me

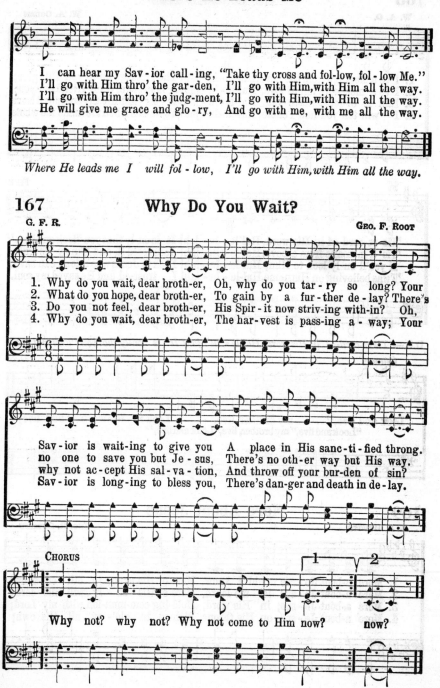

I can hear my Sav-ior call-ing, "Take thy cross and fol-low, fol-low Me."
I'll go with Him thro' the gar-den, I'll go with Him, with Him all the way.
I'll go with Him thro' the judg-ment, I'll go with Him, with Him all the way.
He will give me grace and glo-ry, And go with me, with me all the way.

Where He leads me I will fol-low, I'll go with Him, with Him all the way.

167   Why Do You Wait?

G. F. R.   GEO. F. ROOT

1. Why do you wait, dear broth-er, Oh, why do you tar-ry so long? Your
2. What do you hope, dear broth-er, To gain by a fur-ther de-lay? There's
3. Do you not feel, dear broth-er, His Spir-it now striv-ing with-in? Oh,
4. Why do you wait, dear broth-er, The har-vest is pass-ing a-way; Your

Sav-ior is wait-ing to give you A place in His sanc-ti-fied throng.
no one to save you but Je-sus, There's no oth-er way but His way.
why not ac-cept His sal-va-tion, And throw off your bur-den of sin?
Sav-ior is long-ing to bless you, There's dan-ger and death in de-lay.

CHORUS

Why not? why not? Why not come to Him now?   now?

168   Look and Live

W. A. O.

W. A. OGDEN

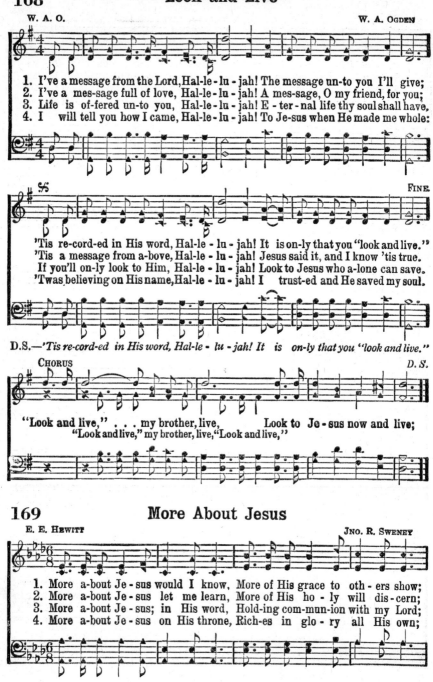

1. I've a message from the Lord, Hal-le - lu - jah! The message un-to you I'll give;
2. I've a mes-sage full of love, Hal-le - lu - jah! A mes-sage, O my friend, for you;
3. Life is of-fered un-to you, Hal-le - lu - jah! E - ter - nal life thy soul shall have,
4. I will tell you how I came, Hal-le - lu - jah! To Je-sus when He made me whole:

'Tis re-cord-ed in His word, Hal-le - lu - jah! It is on-ly that you "look and live."
'Tis a message from a-bove, Hal-le - lu - jah! Jesus said it, and I know 'tis true.
If you'll on-ly look to Him, Hal-le - lu - jah! Look to Jesus who a-lone can save.
'Twas believing on His name, Hal-le - lu - jah! I trust-ed and He saved my soul.

FINE

D.S.—*'Tis re-cord-ed in His word, Hal-le - lu - jah! It is on-ly that you "look and live."*

CHORUS

D.S.

"Look and live," . . . my brother, live,   Look to Je - sus now and live;
"Look and live," my brother, live, "Look and live,"

169   More About Jesus

E. E. HEWITT

JNO. R. SWENEY

1. More a-bout Je-sus would I know, More of His grace to oth - ers show;
2. More a-bout Je-sus let me learn, More of His ho - ly will dis-cern;
3. More a-bout Je-sus; in His word, Hold-ing com-mun-ion with my Lord;
4. More a-bout Je-sus on His throne, Rich-es in glo - ry all His own;

More About Jesus

More of His sav-ing full-ness see, More of His love who died for me.
Spir-it of God, my teach-er be, Show-ing the things of Christ to me.
Hear-ing His voice in ev-'ry line, Mak-ing each faith-ful say-ing mine.
More of His king-dom's sure in-crease; More of His com-ing, Prince of Peace.

D.S.—*More of His sav-ing full-ness see, More of His love who died for me.*

REFRAIN   **D. S.**

More, more a-bout Je-sus, More, more a-bout Je-sus;

170 Majestic Sweetness Sits Enthroned

SAMUEL STENNETT   THOMAS HASTINGS

1. Ma-jes-tic sweetness sits enthroned Up-on the Sav-ior's brow; His head with
2. No mor-tal can with Him compare, A-mong the sons of men; Fair-er is
3. He saw me plunged in deep distress, And flew to my re-lief; For me He
4. To Him I owe my life and breath, And all the joys I have; He makes me

radiant glories crowned, His lips with grace o'erflow, His lips with grace o'erflow.
He than all the fair Who fill the heav'nly train, Who fill the heav'nly train.
bore the shameful cross, And carried all my grief, And car-ried all my grief.
tri-umph o-ver death, And saves me from the grave, And saves me from the grave.

171 How Firm a Foundation

George Keith

Anne Steele

1. How firm a foun-da-tion, ye saints of the Lord, Is laid for your
2. In ev-'ry con-di-tion, in sick-ness, in health, In pov-er-ty's
3. "When thro' fi-ery tri-als thy path-way shall lie, My grace, all suf-
4. "E'en down to old age, all My peo-ple shall prove My Sov-'reign, e-
5. "The soul that on Je-sus hath leaned for re-pose, I will not, I

faith in His ex-cel-lent word! What more can He say than to
vale, or a-bound-ing in wealth; At home and a-broad, on the
fi-cient, shall be thy sup-ply; The flame shall not hurt thee;—I
ter-nal, un-change-a-ble love; And when hoar-y hairs shall their
will not de-sert to his foes; That soul, tho' all hell should en-

you He hath said, You who un-to Je-sus for ref-uge have fled?
land, on the sea, As your days may demand, shall your strength ev-er be.
on-ly de-sign Thy dross to con-sume, and thy gold to re-fine.
tem-ples a-dorn, Like lambs they shall still in My bos-om be borne.
deav-or to shake, I'll nev-er, no nev-er, no nev-er for-sake!"

172 Take My Life, and Let It Be

F. R. Havergal

Wm. B. Bradbury

1. Take my life, and let it be   Con-se-crat-ed, Lord, to Thee;
2. Take my feet, and let them be   Swift and beau-ti-ful for Thee;
3. Take my sil-ver and my gold,   Not a mite would I with-hold;
4. Take my will, and make it Thine,   It shall be no lon-ger mine;

Cho.—*Lord, I give my life to Thee, Thine for-ev-er-more to be;*

Take My Life, and Let It Be

D. C. for Chorus

Take my hands and let them move   At the im-pulse of Thy love.
Take my voice, and let me sing   Al-ways, on-ly, for my King.
Take my mo-ments and my days,   Let them flow in cease-less praise.
Take my heart, it is Thine own,   It shall be Thy roy-al throne.

Lord, I give my life to Thee, Thine for-ev-er-more to be.

173   I Need Thee Every Hour

Mrs. ANNIE S. HAWKS   Rev. ROBERT LOWRY

1. I need Thee ev-'ry hour, Most gra-cious Lord; No ten-der voice like
2. I need Thee ev-'ry hour, Stay Thou near by; Temp-ta-tions lose their
3. I need Thee ev-'ry hour, In joy or pain; Come quick-ly and a-
4. I need Thee ev-'ry hour, Most Ho-ly One; O make me Thine in-

CHORUS

Thine Can peace af-ford.
pow'r When Thou art nigh.   I need Thee, O I need Thee; Ev-'ry hour I
bide, Or life is vain.
deed, Thou bless-ed Son!

need Thee! O bless me now, my Sav-ior, I come to Thee!

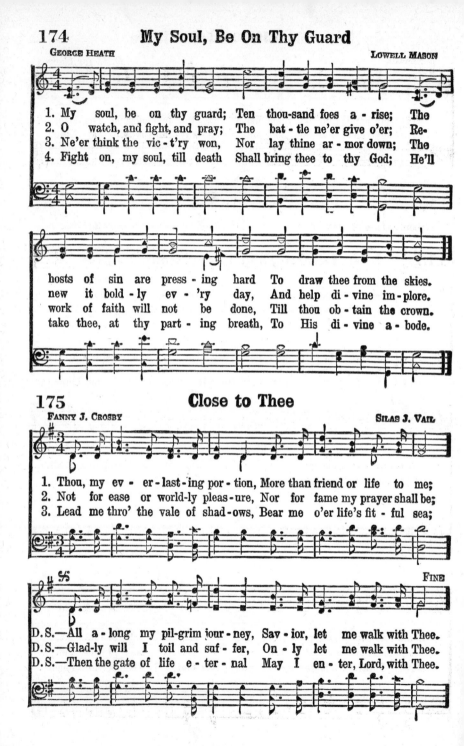

174

My Soul, Be On Thy Guard

GEORGE HEATH

LOWELL MASON

1. My soul, be on thy guard; Ten thou-sand foes a - rise; The
2. O watch, and fight, and pray; The bat - tle ne'er give o'er; Re-
3. Ne'er think the vic - t'ry won, Nor lay thine ar - mor down; The
4. Fight on, my soul, till death Shall bring thee to thy God; He'll

hosts of sin are press - ing hard To draw thee from the skies.
new it bold - ly ev - 'ry day, And help di - vine im - plore.
work of faith will not be done, Till thou ob - tain the crown.
take thee, at thy part - ing breath, To His di - vine a - bode.

175

Close to Thee

FANNY J. CROSBY

SILAS J. VAIL

1. Thou, my ev - er - last - ing por - tion, More than friend or life to me;
2. Not for ease or world-ly pleas - ure, Nor for fame my prayer shall be;
3. Lead me thro' the vale of shad - ows, Bear me o'er life's fit - ful sea;

FINE

D.S.—All a - long my pil-grim jour - ney, Sav - ior, let me walk with Thee.
D.S.—Glad-ly will I toil and suf - fer, On - ly let me walk with Thee.
D.S.—Then the gate of life e - ter - nal May I en - ter, Lord, with Thee.

Close to Thee

D.S.

REFRAIN

Close to Thee, close to Thee, Close to Thee, close to Thee;

176   Jesus, Saviour, Pilot Me

EDWARD HOPPER   J. E. GOULD

1. Je - sus, Sav - ior, pi - lot me O - ver life's tem - pes-tuous seas
2. As a moth - er stills her child, Thou canst hush the o - cean wild;
3. When at last I near the shore, And the fear - ful break-ers roar

Un-known waves be - fore me roll, Hid - ing rocks and treach'rous shoal;
Boist'rous waves o - bey Thy will When Thou say'st to them "Be still!"
'Twixt me and the peace-ful rest, Then, while lean-ing on Thy breast,

Chart and com - pass come from Thee, Je - sus, Sav - ior, pi - lot me.
Won-drous Sov-'reign of the sea, Je - sus, Sav - ior, pi - lot me.
May I hear Thee say to me, "Fear not, I will pi - lot thee."

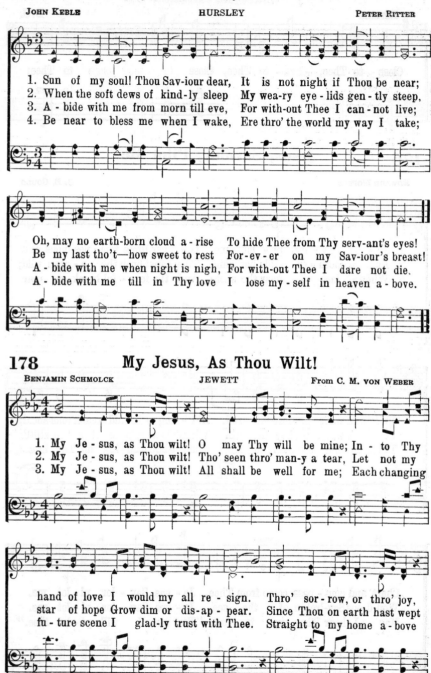

177 Sun of My Soul

JOHN KEBLE   HURSLEY   PETER RITTER

1. Sun of my soul! Thou Sav-iour dear, It is not night if Thou be near;
2. When the soft dews of kind-ly sleep My wea-ry eye - lids gen - tly steep,
3. A - bide with me from morn till eve, For with-out Thee I can - not live;
4. Be near to bless me when I wake, Ere thro' the world my way I take;

Oh, may no earth-born cloud a - rise To hide Thee from Thy serv-ant's eyes!
Be my last tho't—how sweet to rest For-ev - er on my Sav-iour's breast!
A - bide with me when night is nigh, For with-out Thee I dare not die.
A - bide with me till in Thy love I lose my - self in heaven a - bove.

178 My Jesus, As Thou Wilt!

BENJAMIN SCHMOLCK   JEWETT   From C. M. VON WEBER

1. My Je - sus, as Thou wilt! O may Thy will be mine; In - to Thy
2. My Je - sus, as Thou wilt! Tho' seen thro' man-y a tear, Let not my
3. My Je - sus, as Thou wilt! All shall be well for me; Each changing

hand of love I would my all re - sign. Thro' sor - row, or thro' joy,
star of hope Grow dim or dis-ap - pear. Since Thou on earth hast wept
fu - ture scene I glad-ly trust with Thee. Straight to my home a - bove

My Jesus, As Thou Wilt!

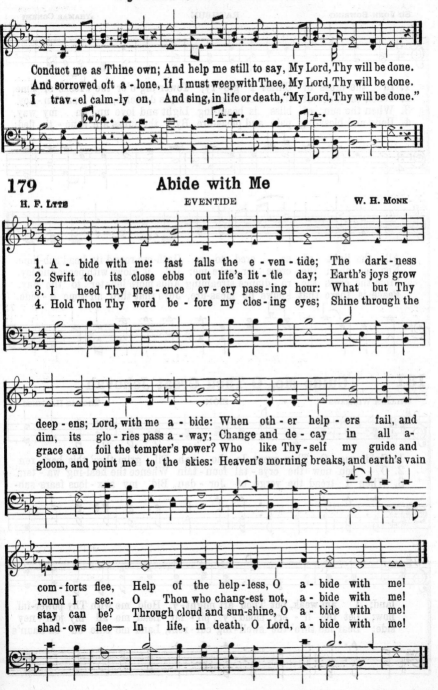

Conduct me as Thine own; And help me still to say, My Lord, Thy will be done.
And sorrowed oft a-lone, If I must weep with Thee, My Lord, Thy will be done.
I trav-el calm-ly on, And sing, in life or death, "My Lord, Thy will be done."

179   Abide with Me

EVENTIDE

H. F. LYTE   W. H. MONK

1. A-bide with me: fast falls the e-ven-tide; The dark-ness
2. Swift to its close ebbs out life's lit-tle day; Earth's joys grow
3. I need Thy pres-ence ev-ery pass-ing hour: What but Thy
4. Hold Thou Thy word be-fore my clos-ing eyes; Shine through the

deep-ens; Lord, with me a-bide: When oth-er help-ers fail, and
dim, its glo-ries pass a-way; Change and de-cay in all a-
grace can foil the tempter's power? Who like Thy-self my guide and
gloom, and point me to the skies: Heaven's morning breaks, and earth's vain

com-forts flee, Help of the help-less, O a-bide with me!
round I see; O Thou who chang-est not, a-bide with me!
stay can be? Through cloud and sun-shine, O a-bide with me!
shad-ows flee— In life, in death, O Lord, a-bide with me!

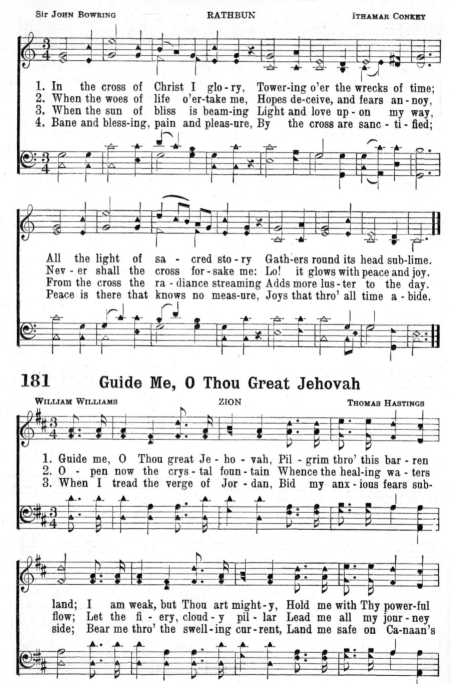

180 · In the Cross of Christ

Sir John Bowring   RATHBUN   Ithamar Conkey

1. In the cross of Christ I glo-ry, Tower-ing o'er the wrecks of time;
2. When the woes of life o'er-take me, Hopes de-ceive, and fears an-noy,
3. When the sun of bliss is beam-ing Light and love up-on my way,
4. Bane and bless-ing, pain and pleas-ure, By the cross are sanc-ti-fied;

All the light of sa-cred sto-ry Gath-ers round its head sub-lime.
Nev-er shall the cross for-sake me: Lo! it glows with peace and joy.
From the cross the ra-diance streaming Adds more lus-ter to the day.
Peace is there that knows no meas-ure, Joys that thro' all time a-bide.

181 · Guide Me, O Thou Great Jehovah

William Williams   ZION   Thomas Hastings

1. Guide me, O Thou great Je-ho-vah, Pil-grim thro' this bar-ren
2. O-pen now the crys-tal foun-tain Whence the heal-ing wa-ters
3. When I tread the verge of Jor-dan, Bid my anx-ious fears sub-

land; I am weak, but Thou art might-y, Hold me with Thy power-ful
flow; Let the fi-ery, cloud-y pil-lar Lead me all my jour-ney
side; Bear me thro' the swell-ing cur-rent, Land me safe on Ca-naan's

Guide Me, O Thou Great Jehovah

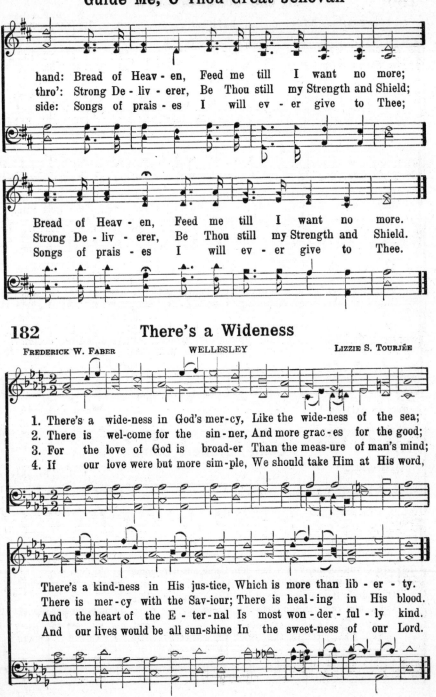

hand: Bread of Heav - en, Feed me till I want no more;
thro': Strong De - liv - erer, Be Thou still my Strength and Shield;
side: Songs of prais - es I will ev - er give to Thee;

Bread of Heav - en, Feed me till I want no more.
Strong De - liv - erer, Be Thou still my Strength and Shield.
Songs of prais - es I will ev - er give to Thee.

182   There's a Wideness

FREDERICK W. FABER   WELLESLEY   LIZZIE S. TOURJÉE

1. There's a wide-ness in God's mer-cy, Like the wide-ness of the sea;
2. There is wel-come for the sin-ner, And more grac-es for the good;
3. For the love of God is broad-er Than the meas-ure of man's mind;
4. If our love were but more sim-ple, We should take Him at His word,

There's a kind-ness in His jus-tice, Which is more than lib - er - ty.
There is mer - cy with the Sav-iour; There is heal-ing in His blood.
And the heart of the E - ter-nal Is most won - der - ful - ly kind.
And our lives would be all sun-shine In the sweet-ness of our Lord.

Almost Persuaded

P. P. B.

P. P. BLISS

1. "Al - most per-suad - ed," now to be - lieve; "Al - most per-suad - ed,"
2. "Al - most per-suad - ed," come, come to - day; "Al - most per-suad - ed,"
3. "Al - most per-suad - ed," har - vest is past! "Al - most per-suad - ed,"

Christ to re - ceive; Seems now some soul to say, "Go, Spir - it,
turn not a - way; Je - sus in - vites you here, An - gels are
doom comes at last! "Al - most" can - not a - vail; "Al - most" is

go Thy way, Some more con - ven - ient day On Thee I'll call."
lin-g'ring near, Prayers rise from hearts so dear, O wan-d'rer, come.
but to fail! Sad, sad, that bit - ter wail, "Al - most," but lost.

184

Come, Sinner, Come

W. E. WITTER

H. R. PALMER

1. { While Je - sus whis-pers to you, Come, sin-ner, come!
     { While we are pray-ing for you,(Omit . . . . .) Come, sin-ner, come!
2. { Are you too heav - y - la - den, Come, sin-ner, come!
     { Je - sus will bear your bur-den,(Omit . . . . .) Come, sin-ner, come!
3. { Oh, hear His ten-der plead-ing, Come, sin-ner, come!
     { Come and re-ceive the bless-ing,(Omit . . . . .) Come, sin-ner, come!

Come, Sinner, Come

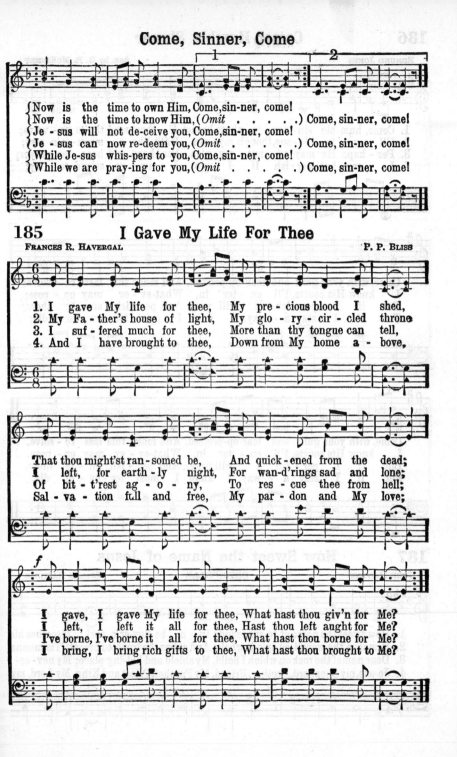

{ Now is the time to own Him, Come, sin-ner, come!
{ Now is the time to know Him, (*Omit* . . . . .) Come, sin-ner, come!
{ Je - sus will not de-ceive you, Come, sin-ner, come!
{ Je - sus can now re-deem you, (*Omit* . . . . .) Come, sin-ner, come!
{ While Je-sus whis-pers to you, Come, sin-ner, come!
{ While we are pray-ing for you, (*Omit* . . . . .) Come, sin-ner, come!

185 I Gave My Life For Thee

Frances R. Havergal

P. P. Bliss

1. I gave My life for thee, My pre-cious blood I shed,
2. My Fa-ther's house of light, My glo-ry-cir-cled throne
3. I suf-fered much for thee, More than thy tongue can tell,
4. And I have brought to thee, Down from My home a-bove,

That thou might'st ran-somed be, And quick-ened from the dead;
I left, for earth-ly night, For wan-d'rings sad and lone;
Of bit-t'rest ag-o-ny, To res-cue thee from hell;
Sal-va-tion full and free, My par-don and My love;

I gave, I gave My life for thee, What hast thou giv'n for Me?
I left, I left it all for thee, Hast thou left aught for Me?
I've borne, I've borne it all for thee, What hast thou borne for Me?
I bring, I bring rich gifts to thee, What hast thou brought to Me?

186

Come, Humble Sinner

EDMUND JONES

Arr. by B. B. McKINNEY

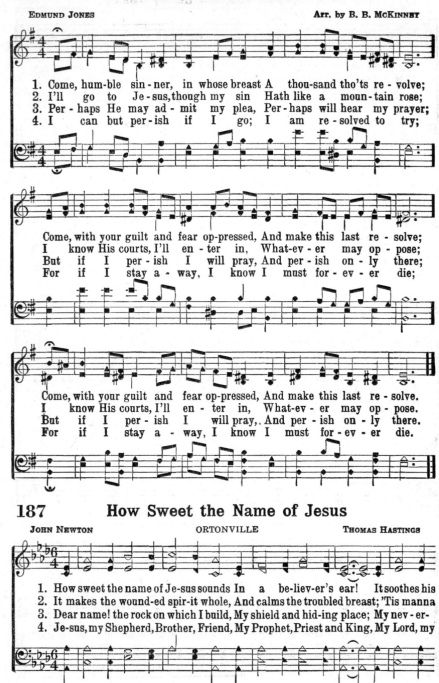

1. Come, hum-ble sin-ner, in whose breast A thou-sand tho'ts re-volve;
2. I'll go to Je-sus, though my sin Hath like a moun-tain rose;
3. Per-haps He may ad-mit my plea, Per-haps will hear my prayer;
4. I can but per-ish if I go; I am re-solved to try;

Come, with your guilt and fear op-pressed, And make this last re-solve;
I know His courts, I'll en-ter in, What-ev-er may op-pose;
But if I per-ish I will pray, And per-ish on-ly there;
For if I stay a-way, I know I must for-ev-er die;

Come, with your guilt and fear op-pressed, And make this last re-solve.
I know His courts, I'll en-ter in, What-ev-er may op-pose.
But if I per-ish I will pray, And per-ish on-ly there.
For if I stay a-way, I know I must for-ev-er die.

187

How Sweet the Name of Jesus

JOHN NEWTON

ORTONVILLE

THOMAS HASTINGS

1. How sweet the name of Je-sus sounds In a be-liev-er's ear! It soothes his
2. It makes the wound-ed spir-it whole, And calms the troubled breast; 'Tis manna
3. Dear name! the rock on which I build, My shield and hid-ing place; My nev-er-
4. Je-sus, my Shepherd, Brother, Friend, My Prophet, Priest and King, My Lord, my

How Sweet the Name of Jesus

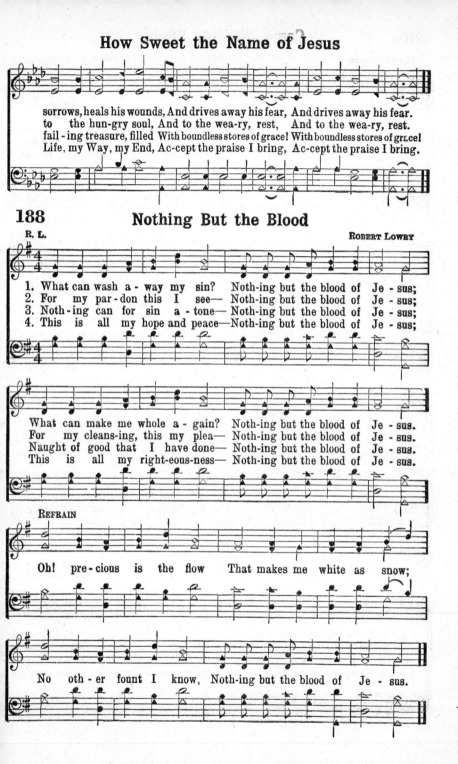

sorrows, heals his wounds, And drives away his fear, And drives away his fear.
to   the hun-gry soul, And to the wea-ry, rest,   And to the wea-ry, rest.
fail - ing treasure, filled With boundless stores of grace! With boundless stores of grace!
Life, my Way, my End, Ac-cept the praise I bring, Ac-cept the praise I bring.

188   **Nothing But the Blood**

R. L.
ROBERT LOWRY

1. What can wash a - way my sin? Noth-ing but the blood of Je - sus;
2. For my par - don this I   see— Noth-ing but the blood of Je - sus;
3. Noth - ing can for sin a - tone— Noth-ing but the blood of Je - sus;
4. This is all my hope and peace—Noth-ing but the blood of Je - sus;

What can make me whole a - gain? Noth-ing but the blood of Je - sus.
For   my cleans-ing, this my plea— Noth-ing but the blood of Je - sus.
Naught of good that I have done— Noth-ing but the blood of Je - sus.
This is   all   my right-eous-ness— Noth-ing but the blood of Je - sus.

REFRAIN

Oh! pre - cious is   the   flow   That makes me   white as   snow;

No   oth - er fount I   know, Noth-ing but the blood of   Je - sus.

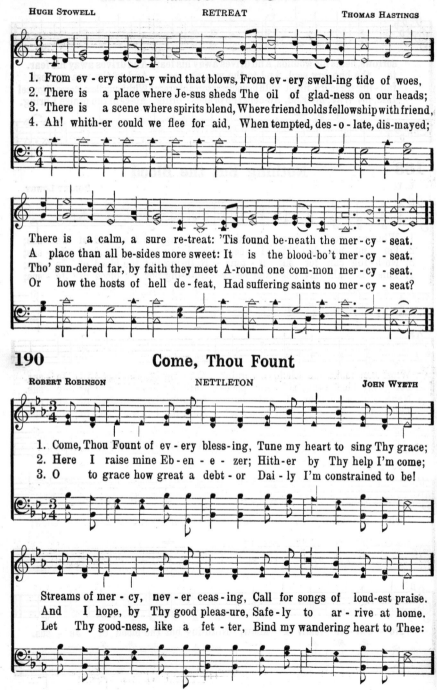

189 From Every Stormy Wind

HUGH STOWELL
RETREAT
THOMAS HASTINGS

1. From ev-ery storm-y wind that blows, From ev-ery swell-ing tide of woes,
2. There is a place where Je-sus sheds The oil of glad-ness on our heads;
3. There is a scene where spirits blend, Where friend holds fellowship with friend,
4. Ah! whith-er could we flee for aid, When tempted, des-o-late, dis-mayed;

There is a calm, a sure re-treat: 'Tis found be-neath the mer-cy - seat.
A place than all be-sides more sweet: It is the blood-bo't mer-cy - seat.
Tho' sun-dered far, by faith they meet A-round one com-mon mer-cy - seat.
Or how the hosts of hell de-feat, Had suffering saints no mer-cy - seat?

190 Come, Thou Fount

ROBERT ROBINSON
NETTLETON
JOHN WYETH

1. Come, Thou Fount of ev-ery bless-ing, Tune my heart to sing Thy grace;
2. Here I raise mine Eb-en-e-zer; Hith-er by Thy help I'm come;
3. O to grace how great a debt-or Dai-ly I'm constrained to be!

Streams of mer-cy, nev-er ceas-ing, Call for songs of loud-est praise.
And I hope, by Thy good pleas-ure, Safe-ly to ar-rive at home.
Let Thy good-ness, like a fet-ter, Bind my wandering heart to Thee:

Come, Thou Fount

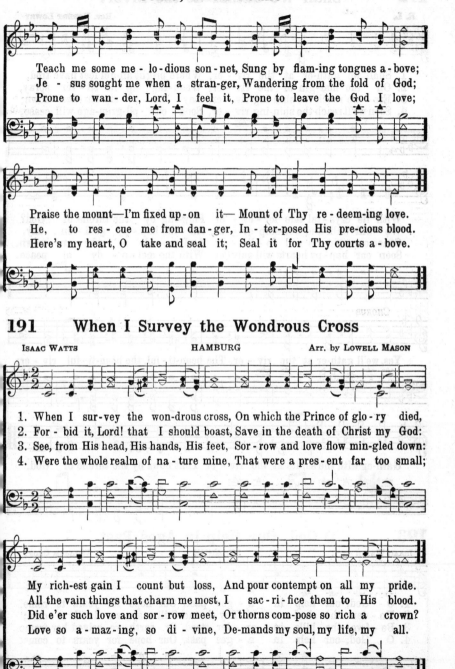

Teach me some me - lo - dious son - net, Sung by flam-ing tongues a - bove;
Je - sus sought me when a stran-ger, Wandering from the fold of God;
Prone to wan - der, Lord, I feel it, Prone to leave the God I love;

Praise the mount—I'm fixed up-on it— Mount of Thy re - deem-ing love.
He, to res - cue me from dan-ger, In - ter-posed His pre-cious blood.
Here's my heart, O take and seal it; Seal it for Thy courts a - bove.

191 When I Survey the Wondrous Cross

ISAAC WATTS   HAMBURG   Arr. by LOWELL MASON

1. When I sur-vey the won-drous cross, On which the Prince of glo - ry died,
2. For - bid it, Lord! that I should boast, Save in the death of Christ my God:
3. See, from His head, His hands, His feet, Sor - row and love flow min-gled down:
4. Were the whole realm of na - ture mine, That were a pres - ent far too small;

My rich-est gain I count but loss, And pour contempt on all my pride.
All the vain things that charm me most, I sac - ri - fice them to His blood.
Did e'er such love and sor - row meet, Or thorns com-pose so rich a crown?
Love so a - maz - ing, so di - vine, De-mands my soul, my life, my all.

192 Shall We Gather at the River?

R. L.

Rev. Robert Lowry

1. Shall we gath-er at the riv - er, Where bright an-gel feet have trod;
2. On the mar-gin of the riv - er, Wash-ing up its sil - ver spray,
3. Ere we reach the shin-ing riv - er, Lay we ev - ery bur-den down;
4. Soon we'll reach the shin-ing riv - er, Soon our pil-grim-age will cease,

With its crys-tal tide for - ev - er Flow-ing by the throne of God?
We will walk and wor-ship ev - er, All the hap - py gold - en day.
Grace our spir-its will de - liv - er, And pro-vide a robe and crown.
Soon our hap - py hearts will quiv - er With the mel - o - dy of peace.

CHORUS

Yes, we'll gath-er at the riv - er, The beau-ti - ful, the beau-ti-ful riv - er;

Gath-er with the saints at the riv - er That flows by the throne of God.

193 O God, Our Help in Ages Past

ISAAC WATTS

ST. ANNE

WILLIAM CROFT

1. O God, our help in a - ges past, Our hope for years to come,
2. Un - der the shad - ow of Thy throne Still may we dwell se - cure;
3. Be - fore the hills in or - der stood, Or earth re - ceived her frame,
4. O God, our help in a - ges past, Our hope for years to come;

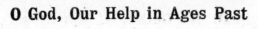

O God, Our Help in Ages Past

Our shel - ter from the storm - y blast, And our e - ter - nal home!
Suf - fi - cient is Thine arm a - lone, And our de - fense is sure.
From ev - er - last - ing Thou art God, To end - less years the same.
Be Thou my guide while life shall last, And our e - ter - nal home.

194

Jesus Paid It All

Mrs. H. M. Hall

John T. Grape

1. I hear the Sav-iour say, "Thy strength in - deed is small, Child of
2. Lord, now in - deed I find Thy power, and Thine a - lone, Can
3. For noth - ing good have I Where-by Thy grace to claim—I'll
4. And when, be - fore the throne, I stand in Him com-plete, "Je - sus

Chorus

weak-ness, watch and pray, Find in Me thine all in all."
change the lep-er's spots, And melt the heart of stone. Je - sus paid it all,
wash my garments white In the blood of Calvary's Lamb.
died my soul to save," My lips shall still re - peat.

All to Him I owe; Sin had left a crimson stain, He washed it white as snow.

195 O Jesus, I Have Promised

JOHN E. BODE

ARTHUR H. MANN

1. O Je-sus, I have prom-ised To serve Thee to the end; Be Thou for-ev - er
2. O let me feel Thee near me, The world is ev - er near; I see the sights that
3. O Je-sus, Thou hast promised To all who fol - low Thee, That where Thou art in

near me, My Mas-ter and my Friend: I shall not fear the bat - tle If Thou art
daz - zle, The tempting sounds I hear: My foes are ev - er near me, A-round me
glo - ry, There shall Thy servant be; And, Je-sus, I have promised To serve Thee

by my side, Nor wan-der from the path-way If Thou wilt be my guide.
and with - in; But, Je - sus, draw Thou near-er, And shield my soul from sin.
to the end; O give me grace to fol - low My Mas - ter and my Friend.

196 I Love Thy Kingdom, Lord

TIMOTHY DWIGHT

AARON WILLIAMS, Coll.

1. I love Thy king - dom, Lord, The house of Thine a - bode,
2. I love Thy Church, O God! Her walls be - fore Thee stand,
3. For her my tears shall fall; For her my prayers as - cend;
4. Be - yond my high - est joy I prize her heav'n-ly ways,
5. Sure as Thy truth shall last, To Zi - on shall be giv'n

I Love Thy Kingdom, Lord

The Church our blest Re-deem-er saved With His own pre-cious blood.
Dear as the ap-ple of Thine eye, And grav-en on Thy hand.
To her my cares and toils be given, Till toils and cares shall end.
Her sweet com-mun-ion, sol-emn vows, Her hymns of love and praise.
The bright-est glo-ries earth can yield, And bright-er bliss of heaven.

197   ## Only Trust Him

J. H. S.   J. H. STOCKTON

1. Come, ev-ery soul by sin op-pressed, There's mer-cy with the Lord,
2. For Je-sus shed His pre-cious blood, Rich bless-ings to be-stow;
3. Yes, Je-sus is the Truth, the Way, That leads you in-to rest;
4. Come, then, and join this ho-ly band, And on to glo-ry go,

And He will sure-ly give you rest By trust-ing in His word.
Plunge now in-to the crim-son flood That wash-es white as snow.
Be-lieve in Him with-out de-lay, And you are ful-ly blest.
To dwell in that ce-les-tial land, Where joys im-mor-tal flow.

CHORUS.

On-ly trust Him, on-ly trust Him, On-ly trust Him now;
He will save you, He will save you, He will (*Omit.* . . .) save you now.

My Faith Looks Up to Thee

Ray Palmer.   *Olivet. 6. 4.*   Lowell Mason.

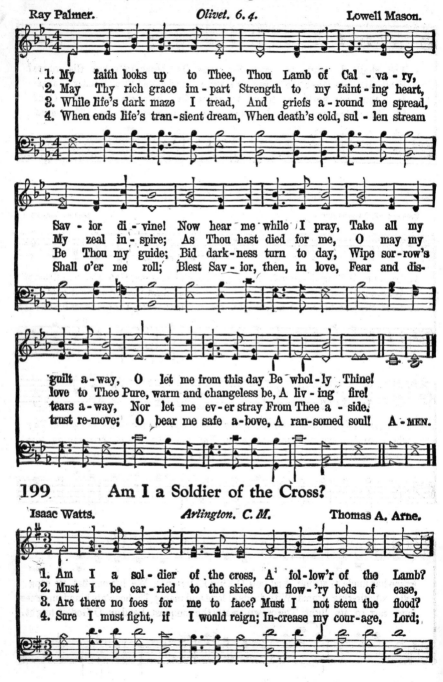

1. My faith looks up to Thee, Thou Lamb of Cal - va - ry,
2. May Thy rich grace im - part Strength to my faint - ing heart,
3. While life's dark maze I tread, And griefs a - round me spread,
4. When ends life's tran - sient dream, When death's cold, sul - len stream

Sav - ior di - vine! Now hear me while I pray, Take all my
My zeal in - spire; As Thou hast died for me, O may my
Be Thou my guide; Bid dark - ness turn to day, Wipe sor - row's
Shall o'er me roll; Blest Sav - ior, then, in love, Fear and dis-

guilt a - way, O let me from this day Be whol - ly Thine!
love to Thee Pure, warm and changeless be, A liv - ing fire!
tears a - way, Nor let me ev - er stray From Thee a - side.
trust re - move; O bear me safe a - bove, A ran - somed soul! A - MEN.

199   Am I a Soldier of the Cross?

Isaac Watts.   *Arlington. C. M.*   Thomas A. Arne.

1. Am I a sol - dier of the cross, A fol - low'r of the Lamb?
2. Must I be car - ried to the skies On flow - 'ry beds of ease,
3. Are there no foes for me to face? Must I not stem the flood?
4. Sure I must fight, if I would reign; In - crease my cour - age, Lord;

Am I a Soldier of the Cross?

And shall I fear to own His cause, Or blush to speak His name?
While oth-ers fought to win the prize, And sailed thro' blood-y seas?
Is this vile world a friend to grace, To help me on to God?
I'll bear the toil, en-dure the pain, Sup-port-ed by Thy word.

200 Lead On, O King Eternal

Ernest W. Shurtleff

Henry Smart

1. Lead on, O King E-ter-nal, The day of march has come; Henceforth in fields of
2. Lead on, O King E-ter-nal, Till sin's fierce war shall cease, And ho-li-ness shall
3. Lead on, O King E-ter-nal, We fol-low, not with fears; For gladness breaks like

con-quest Thy tents shall be our home. Thro' days of prep-a-ra-tion Thy
whis-per The sweet A-men of peace; For not with swords loud clashing, Nor
morn-ing Where'er Thy face ap-pears; Thy cross is lift-ed o'er us; We

grace has made us strong, And now, O King E-ter-nal, We lift our bat-tle song.
roll of stir-ring drums; With deeds of love and mercy, The heav'nly kingdom comes.
jour-ney in its light: The crown awaits the conquest; Lead on, O God of might.

201 Faith of Our Fathers

FREDERICK W. FABER   ST. CATHERINE   H. F. HEMY

1. Faith of our fa-thers! liv-ing still In spite of dun-geon, fire, and sword:
2. Our fa-thers, chained in pris-ons dark, Were still in heart and conscience free:
3. Faith of our fa-thers! we will love Both friend and foe in all our strife:

O how our hearts beat high with joy When-e'er we hear that glo-rious word!
How sweet would be their children's fate, If they, like them, could die for thee!
And preach thee, too, as love knows how, By kind-ly words and vir-tuous life:

Faith of our fa-thers! ho-ly faith! We will be true to thee till death!
Faith of our fa-thers! ho-ly faith! We will be true to thee till death!
Faith of our fa-thers! ho-ly faith! We will be true to thee till death!

202 O Master, Let Me Walk with Thee

W. GLADDEN   MARYTON   H. P. SMITH

1. O Mas-ter, let me walk with Thee In low-ly paths of serv-ice free;
2. Help me the slow of heart to move By some clear, winning word of love;
3. Teach me Thy patience! still with Thee In clos-er, dear-er com-pa-ny,
4. In hope that sends a shin-ing ray Far down the fu-ture's broadening way,

O Master, Let Me Walk with Thee

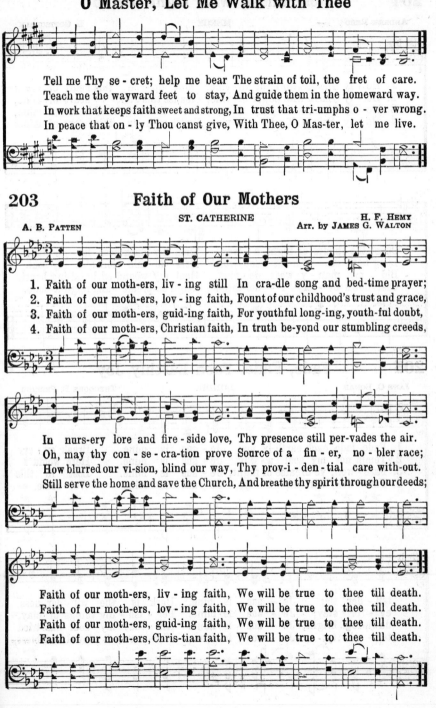

Tell me Thy se-cret; help me bear The strain of toil, the fret of care.
Teach me the wayward feet to stay, And guide them in the homeward way.
In work that keeps faith sweet and strong, In trust that tri-umphs o - ver wrong.
In peace that on - ly Thou canst give, With Thee, O Mas-ter, let me live.

203

Faith of Our Mothers

ST. CATHERINE

A. B. PATTEN

H. F. HEMY
Arr. by JAMES G. WALTON

1. Faith of our moth-ers, liv - ing still In cra-dle song and bed-time prayer;
2. Faith of our moth-ers, lov - ing faith, Fount of our childhood's trust and grace,
3. Faith of our moth-ers, guid-ing faith, For youthful long-ing, youth-ful doubt,
4. Faith of our moth-ers, Christian faith, In truth be-yond our stumbling creeds,

In nurs-ery lore and fire-side love, Thy presence still per-vades the air.
Oh, may thy con - se - cra-tion prove Source of a fin - er, no - bler race;
How blurred our vi-sion, blind our way, Thy prov-i - den-tial care with-out.
Still serve the home and save the Church, And breathe thy spirit through our deeds;

Faith of our moth-ers, liv - ing faith, We will be true to thee till death.
Faith of our moth-ers, lov - ing faith, We will be true to thee till death.
Faith of our moth-ers, guid-ing faith, We will be true to thee till death.
Faith of our moth-ers, Chris-tian faith, We will be true to thee till death.

Holy Ghost, with Light Divine

ANDREW REED   MERCY   L. GOTTSCHALK

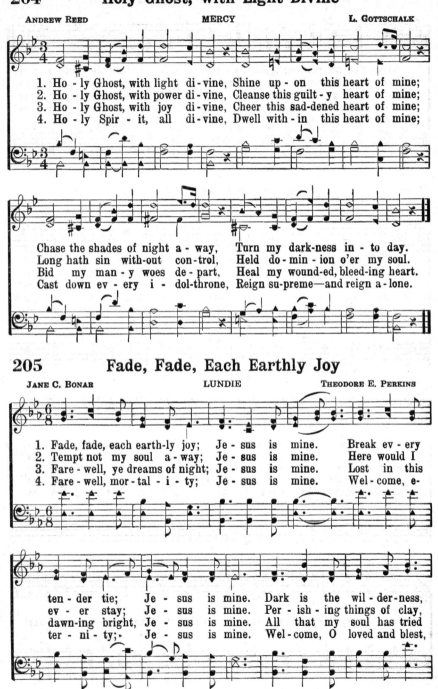

1. Ho - ly Ghost, with light di - vine, Shine up - on this heart of mine;
2. Ho - ly Ghost, with power di - vine, Cleanse this guilt - y heart of mine;
3. Ho - ly Ghost, with joy di - vine, Cheer this sad-dened heart of mine;
4. Ho - ly Spir - it, all di - vine, Dwell with - in this heart of mine;

Chase the shades of night a - way,   Turn my dark-ness in - to day.
Long hath sin with-out con - trol,   Held do - min - ion o'er my soul.
Bid my man - y woes de - part,   Heal my wound-ed, bleed-ing heart.
Cast down ev - ery i - dol-throne,   Reign su-preme—and reign a - lone.

205

Fade, Fade, Each Earthly Joy

JANE C. BONAR   LUNDIE   THEODORE E. PERKINS

1. Fade, fade, each earth-ly joy; Je - sus is mine. Break ev - ery
2. Tempt not my soul a - way; Je - sus is mine. Here would I
3. Fare - well, ye dreams of night; Je - sus is mine. Lost in this
4. Fare - well, mor - tal - i - ty; Je - sus is mine. Wel - come, e -

ten - der tie; Je - sus is mine. Dark is the wil - der-ness,
ev - er stay; Je - sus is mine. Per - ish - ing things of clay,
dawn-ing bright, Je - sus is mine. All that my soul has tried
ter - ni - ty; Je - sus is mine. Wel - come, O loved and blest,

Fade, Fade, Each Earthly Joy

Earth has no rest-ing-place, Je - sus a - lone can bless; Je - sus is mine.
Born but for one brief day, Pass from my heart a - way; Je - sus is mine.
Left but a dis - mal void; Je - sus has sat - is - fied; Je - sus is mine.
Wel - come, sweet scenes of rest, Welcome, my Saviour's breast; Je - sus is mine.

206 Nearer, My God, to Thee

SARAH F. ADAMS   BETHANY   LOWELL MASON

1. Near - er, my God, to Thee, Near - er to Thee! E'en though it
2. Though like the wan - der - er, The sun gone down, Dark - ness be
3. There let the way ap - pear, Steps un - to heaven: All that Thou
4. Then with my wak-ing thoughts Bright with Thy praise, Out of my
5. Or if on joy - ful wing, Cleav-ing the sky, Sun, moon, and

be a cross That rais - eth me; Still all my song shall be,
o - ver me, My rest a stone; Yet in my dreams I'd be
send - est me, In mer - cy given: An - gels to beck - on me
sto - ny griefs Beth - el I'll raise; So by my woes to be
stars for - got, Up - ward I fly, Still all my song shall be,

Near - er, my God, to Thee, Near - er, my God, to Thee, Near - er to Thee!

207 Seal Us, O Holy Spirit

I. H. M.

(Inscribed to my friend, Rev. J. F. Carson, D.D.)

I. H. MEREDITH

Prayerfully

1. Seal us, O Ho-ly Spir-it, Grant us Thine im-press, we pray;
2. Seal us, O Ho-ly Spir-it, Help us Thy like-ness to show;
3. Seal us, O Ho-ly Spir-it, Make us Thine own from this hour;

We would be more like the Sav-iour, Stamped with His im-age to-day.
Then from our lives un-to oth-ers Streams of rich bless-ings shall flow.
Let me be use-ful, dear Mas-ter, Seal us with wit-ness-ing power.

Chorus

Seal us, seal us, Seal us just now, we pray; Seal us, O

rit.

Ho-ly Spir-it, Seal us for serv-ice to-day.

208 Not All the Blood of Beasts

ISAAC WATTS

BOYLSTON

LOWELL MASON

1. Not all the blood of beasts On Jew-ish al-tars slain,
2. But Christ, the heaven-ly Lamb, Takes all our sins a-way;
3. My faith would lay her hand On that dear head of Thine,
4. My soul looks back to see The bur-den Thou didst bear,

Not All the Blood of Beasts

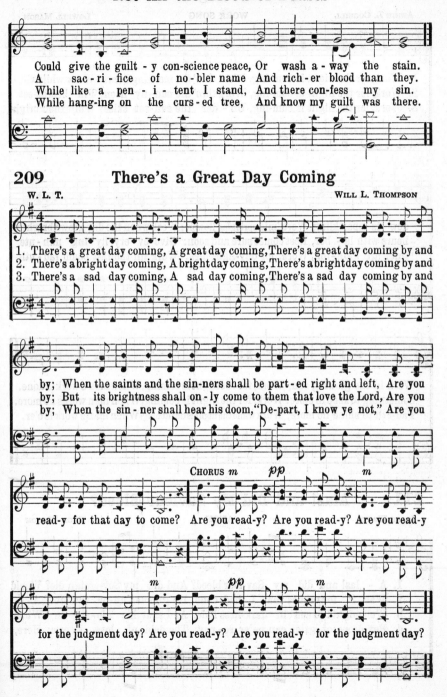

Could give the guilt-y con-science peace, Or wash a-way the stain.
A sac-ri-fice of no-bler name And rich-er blood than they.
While like a pen-i-tent I stand, And there con-fess my sin.
While hang-ing on the curs-ed tree, And know my guilt was there.

209 ## There's a Great Day Coming

W. L. T.   WILL L. THOMPSON

1. There's a great day coming, A great day coming, There's a great day coming by and
2. There's a bright day coming, A bright day coming, There's a bright day coming by and
3. There's a sad day coming, A sad day coming, There's a sad day coming by and

by; When the saints and the sin-ners shall be part-ed right and left, Are you
by; But its brightness shall on-ly come to them that love the Lord, Are you
by; When the sin-ner shall hear his doom, "De-part, I know ye not," Are you

CHORUS *m*   *pp*   *m*

read-y for that day to come? Are you read-y? Are you read-y? Are you read-y

m   *pp*   *m*

for the judgment day? Are you read-y? Are you read-y for the judgment day?

210 Work, for the Night Is Coming

ANNIE L. COGHILL   WORK SONG   LOWELL MASON

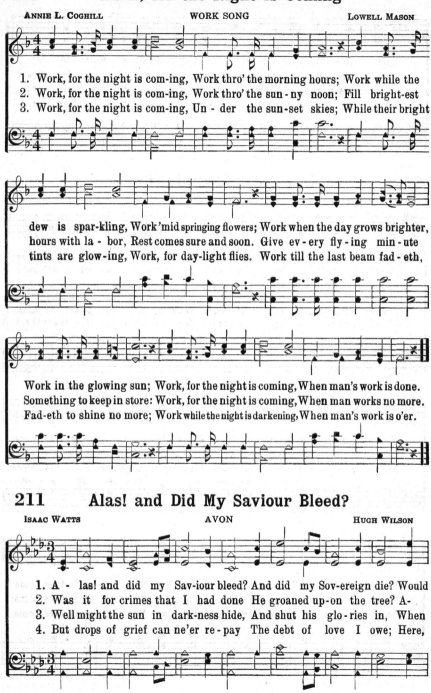

1. Work, for the night is com-ing, Work thro' the morning hours; Work while the
2. Work, for the night is com-ing, Work thro' the sun-ny noon; Fill bright-est
3. Work, for the night is com-ing, Un-der the sun-set skies; While their bright

dew is spar-kling, Work 'mid springing flowers; Work when the day grows brighter,
hours with la-bor, Rest comes sure and soon. Give ev-ery fly-ing min-ute
tints are glow-ing, Work, for day-light flies. Work till the last beam fad-eth,

Work in the glowing sun; Work, for the night is coming, When man's work is done.
Something to keep in store: Work, for the night is coming, When man works no more.
Fad-eth to shine no more; Work while the night is darkening, When man's work is o'er.

211 Alas! and Did My Saviour Bleed?

ISAAC WATTS   AVON   HUGH WILSON

1. A-las! and did my Sav-iour bleed? And did my Sov-ereign die? Would
2. Was it for crimes that I had done He groaned up-on the tree? A-
3. Well might the sun in dark-ness hide, And shut his glo-ries in, When
4. But drops of grief can ne'er re-pay The debt of love I owe; Here,

Alas! and Did My Saviour Bleed?

He de-vote that sa-cred head For such a worm as I?
maz-ing pit-y! grace un-known! And love be-yond de-gree!
Christ, the might-y Mak-er, died For man, the crea-ture's sin.
Lord, I give my-self a-way, 'Tis all that I can do.

212 Holy Spirit, Faithful Guide

MARCUS M. WELLS   FAITHFUL GUIDE   MARCUS M. WELLS

1. { Ho-ly Spir-it, faith-ful Guide, Ev-er near the Chris-tian's side; }
   { Gen-tly lead us by the hand, Pil-grims in a des-ert land; }

2. { Ev-er pres-ent, tru-est Friend, Ev-er near Thine aid to lend, }
   { Leave us not to doubt and fear, Grop-ing on in dark-ness drear; }

3. { When our days of toil shall cease, Wait-ing still for sweet re-lease, }
   { Look-ing up to heaven in prayer, Joy-ful that our names are there: }

Wea-ry souls for-e'er re-joice, While they hear that sweet-est voice,
When the storms are rag-ing sore, Hearts grow faint, and hopes give o'er,
Fear-ing not the dis-mal flood, Plead-ing naught but Je-sus' blood,

Whis-per-ing soft-ly, "Wan-derer, come! Fol-low Me, I'll guide thee home."
Whis-per soft-ly, "Wan-derer, come! Fol-low Me, I'll guide thee home."
Whis-per soft-ly, "Wan-derer, come! Fol-low Me, I'll guide thee home."

213 For the Beauty of the Earth

FOLLIOTT S. PIERPONT   DIX   CONRAD KOCHER

1. For the beau-ty of the earth, For the glo-ry of the skies,
2. For the won-der of each hour Of the day and of the night,
3. For the joy of hu-man love, Broth-er, sis-ter, par-ent, child,
4. For Thy Church that ev-er-more Lift-eth ho-ly hands a-bove,

For the love which from our birth O-ver and a-round us lies;
Hill and vale, and tree and flower, Sun and moon, and stars of light;
Friends on earth, and friends a-bove, For all gen-tle thoughts and mild;
Of-fering up on ev-ery shore Her pure sac-ri-fice of love;

Christ our God, to Thee we raise This our hymn of grate-ful praise
Christ our God, to Thee we raise This our hymn of grate-ful praise.
Christ our God, to Thee we raise This our hymn of grate-ful praise.
Christ our God, to Thee we raise This our hymn of grate-ful praise.

214 Jesus! the Very Thought of Thee

BERNARD   ST. AGNES   J. B. DYKES

1. Je-sus! the ver-y thought of Thee With sweet-ness fills my breast;
2. No voice can sing, no heart can frame, Nor can the mem-ory find,
3. O Hope of ev-ery con-trite heart, O Joy of all the meek,
4. But what to those who find? Ah! this Nor tongue nor pen can show:

Jesus! the Very Thought of Thee

But sweet-er far Thy face to see, And in Thy pres-ence rest.
A sweet-er sound than Je-sus' name, The Sav-iour of man-kind.
To those who ask, how kind Thou art! How good to those who seek!
The love of Je-sus, what it is None but His loved ones know.

215

Fairest Lord Jesus

Crusaders' Hymn

Arr. by RICHARD S. WILLIS

1. Fair-est Lord Je-sus! Rul-er of all na-ture!
2. Fair are the mead-ows, Fair-er still the wood-lands,
3. Fair is the sun-shine, Fair-er still the moon-light,

O Thou of God and man the Son! Thee will I cher-ish,
Robed in the bloom-ing garb of spring; Je-sus is fair-er,
And all the twin-kling star-ry host; Je-sus shines bright-er,

Thee will I hon-or, Thou, my soul's glo-ry, joy, and crown!
Je-sus is pur-er, Who makes the woe-ful heart to sing!
Je-sus shines pur-er, Than all the an-gels heaven can boast!

Holy Bible, Book Divine

JOHN BURTON   ALETTA   WM. B. BRADBURY

1. Ho - ly Bi - ble, Book di - vine, Pre - cious treas-ure, thou art mine;
2. Mine to chide me when I rove; Mine to show a Sav-iour's love;
3. Mine to com - fort in dis - tress, Suf-fering in this wil - der - ness;
4. Mine to tell of joys to come, And the reb - el sin - ner's doom;

Mine to tell me whence I came; Mine to teach me what I am;
Mine thou art to guide and guard; Mine to pun - ish or re - ward;
Mine to show, by liv - ing faith, Man can tri - umph o - ver death;
O thou ho - ly Book di - vine, Pre - cious treas-ure, thou art mine.

217

Lead, Kindly Light

JOHN H. NEWMAN   LUX BENIGNA   JOHN B. DYKES

1. Lead, kind-ly Light, a-mid th' en-cir-cling gloom, Lead Thou me on!
2. I was not ev - er thus, nor prayed that Thou Shouldst lead me on;
3. So long Thy power hath blest me, sure it still Will lead me on

The night is dark, and I am far from home; Lead Thou me on!
I loved to choose and see my path; but now Lead Thou me on!
O'er moor and fen, o'er crag and tor-rent, till The night is gone,

Lead, Kindly Light

Keep Thou my feet; I do not ask to see . . . . .
I loved the gar-ish day, and, spite of fears, ...
And with the morn those an-gel fa-ces smile, ...

The dis-tant scene; one step e-nough for me.
Pride ruled my will. Re-mem-ber not past years.
Which I have loved long since, and lost a-while!

218   Blest Be the Tie

JOHN FAWCETT

HANS G. NÄGELI

1. Blest be the tie that binds Our hearts in Chris-tian love;
2. Be-fore our Fa-ther's throne, We pour our ar-dent prayers;
3. We share our mu-tual woes, Our mu-tual bur-dens bear;
4. When we a-sun-der part, It gives us in-ward pain;

The fel-low-ship of kin-dred minds Is like to that a-bove.
Our fears, our hopes, our aims are one, Our com-forts and our cares.
And oft-en for each oth-er flows The sym-pa-thiz-ing tear.
But we shall still be joined in heart, And hope to meet a-gain.

219 O Love That Wilt Not Let Me Go

GEORGE MATHESON   MARGARET   A. L. PEACE

1. O Love that wilt not let me go, I rest my wea-ry
2. O Light that fol-lowest all my way, I yield my flick-ering
3. O Joy that seek-est me through pain, I can-not close my
4. O Cross that lift-est up my head, I dare not ask to

soul in Thee; I give Thee back the life I owe, That
torch to Thee; My heart re-stores its bor-rowed ray, That
heart to Thee; I trace the rain-bow through the rain, And
hide from Thee; I lay in dust life's glo-ry dead, And

in Thine o-cean depths its flow May rich-er, full-er be.
in Thy sun-shine's glow its day May bright-er, fair-er be.
feel the prom-ise is not vain That morn shall tear-less be.
from the ground there blos-soms red Life that shall end-less be.

220 Bread of Heaven, On Thee We Feed

JOSIAH CONDER   HOLLEY   G. HEWS

1. Bread of heaven, on Thee we feed, For Thy flesh is meat in-deed:
2. Vine of heaven, Thy blood sup-plies This blest cup of sac-ri-fice:
3. Day by day, with strength sup-plied Thro' the life of Him who died,

Bread of Heaven, On Thee We Feed

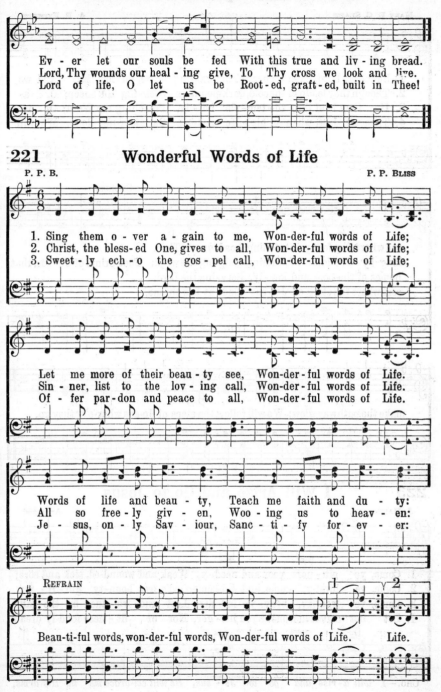

Ev - er let our souls be fed With this true and liv - ing bread.
Lord, Thy wounds our heal - ing give, To Thy cross we look and live.
Lord of life, O let us be Root - ed, graft - ed, built in Thee!

221   **Wonderful Words of Life**

P. P. B.   P. P. BLISS

1. Sing them o - ver a - gain to me, Won-der-ful words of Life;
2. Christ, the bless-ed One, gives to all, Won-der-ful words of Life;
3. Sweet-ly ech-o the gos-pel call, Won-der-ful words of Life;

Let me more of their beau - ty see, Won-der-ful words of Life.
Sin - ner, list to the lov - ing call, Won-der-ful words of Life.
Of - fer par-don and peace to all, Won-der-ful words of Life.

Words of life and beau - ty, Teach me faith and du - ty:
All so free-ly giv - en, Woo-ing us to heav - en:
Je - sus, on - ly Sav - iour, Sanc-ti - fy for-ev - er:

REFRAIN

Beau-ti-ful words, won-der-ful words, Won-der-ful words of Life. Life.

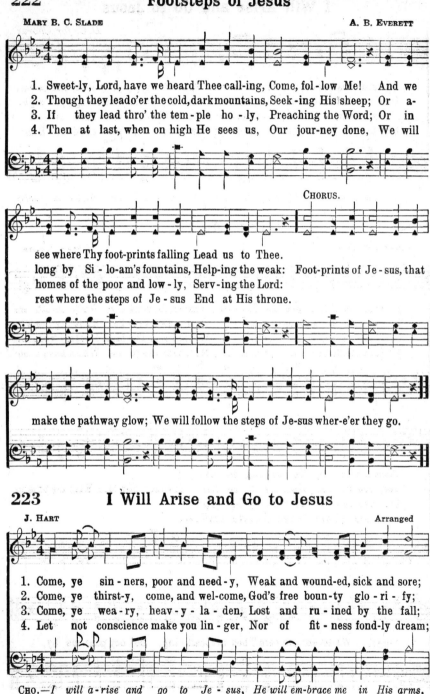

222 **Footsteps of Jesus**

Mary B. C. Slade   A. B. Everett

1. Sweet-ly, Lord, have we heard Thee call-ing, Come, fol-low Me! And we
2. Though they lead o'er the cold, dark mountains, Seek-ing His sheep; Or a-
3. If they lead thro' the tem-ple ho-ly, Preaching the Word; Or in
4. Then at last, when on high He sees us, Our jour-ney done, We will

CHORUS.

see where Thy foot-prints falling Lead us to Thee.
long by Si-lo-am's fountains, Help-ing the weak: Foot-prints of Je-sus, that
homes of the poor and low-ly, Serv-ing the Lord:
rest where the steps of Je-sus End at His throne.

make the pathway glow; We will follow the steps of Je-sus wher-e'er they go.

223 **I Will Arise and Go to Jesus**

J. Hart   Arranged

1. Come, ye sin-ners, poor and need-y, Weak and wound-ed, sick and sore;
2. Come, ye thirst-y, come, and wel-come, God's free boun-ty glo-ri-fy;
3. Come, ye wea-ry, heav-y-la-den, Lost and ru-ined by the fall;
4. Let not conscience make you lin-ger, Nor of fit-ness fond-ly dream;

Cho.—*I will a-rise and go to Je-sus, He will em-brace me in His arms,*

I Will Arise and Go to Jesus

D.C. for Chorus

Je - sus read - y stands to save you, Full of pit - y, love and power.
True be - lief and true re - pent-ance, Ev - ery grace that brings you nigh.
If you tar - ry till you're bet - ter, You will nev - er come at all.
All the fit - ness He re - quir-eth Is to feel your need of Him.

In the arms of my dear Sav-iour, Oh, there are ten thou-sand charms.

224 Pass Me Not

Fanny J. Crosby

W. H. Doane

1. Pass me not, O gen - tle Sav - iour, Hear my humble cry; While on oth - ers
2. Let me at a throne of mer - cy Find a sweet re - lief; Kneeling there in
3. Trust - ing on - ly in Thy mer - it, Would I seek Thy face; Heal my wounded,
4. Thou the Spring of all my com-fort, More than life to me, Whom have I on

Thou art call-ing, Do not pass me by.
deep con-tri-tion, Help my un - be - lief. Sav-iour, Sav-iour, Hear my humble
bro - ken spir - it, Save me by Thy grace.
earth beside Thee? Whom in heaven but Thee?

Chorus

cry; While on oth - ers Thou art call - ing, Do not pass me by.

225

Near to the Heart of God

C. B. McA.

C. B. McAfee

1. There is a place of qui - et rest, Near to the heart of God,
2. There is a place of com - fort sweet, Near to the heart of God,
3. There is a place of full re - lease, Near to the heart of God,

A place where sin can - not mo - lest, Near to the heart of God.
A place where we our Sav - iour meet, Near to the heart of God.
A place where all is joy and peace, Near to the heart of God.

REFRAIN

O Je - sus, blest Re - deem - er, Sent from the heart of God,

Hold us, who wait be - fore Thee, Near to the heart of God.

226

My Prayer

P. P. B.

P. P. BLISS

1. More ho - li-ness give me, More striv-ing with-in; More pa-tience in
2. More grat - i-tude give me, More trust in the Lord; More pride in His
3. More pu - ri - ty give me, More strength to o'er-come; More free-dom from

My Prayer

suf-fering, More sor-row for sin; More faith in my Sav-iour,
glo-ry, More hope in His Word; More tears for His sor-rows,
earth-stains, More long-ings for home; More fit for the king-dom,

More sense of His care; More joy in His serv-ice, More pur-pose in prayer.
More pain at His grief; More meekness in tri-al, More praise for re-lief.
More used would I be; More bless-ed and ho-ly, More, Sav-iour, like Thee.

227 More Love to Thee

ELIZABETH PRENTISS

W. H. DOANE

1. More love to Thee, O Christ, More love to Thee! Hear Thou the
2. Once earth-ly joy I craved, Sought peace and rest; Now Thee a-
3. Then shall my lat-est breath Whis-per Thy praise; This be the

prayer I make On bend-ed knee; This is my ear-nest plea:
lone I seek, Give what is best; This all my prayer shall be;
part-ing cry My heart shall raise; This still its prayer shall be;

More love, O Christ, to Thee, More love to Thee, More love to Thee!

228   Trusting Jesus

E. Page

Ira D. Sankey

1. Sim - ply trust - ing ev - ery day, Trust - ing through a storm - y way;
2. Bright-ly doth His Spir - it shine In - to this poor heart of mine;
3. Sing - ing if my way is clear: Pray - ing if the path be drear;
4. Trust - ing Him while life shall last, Trust - ing Him till earth be past;

E - ven when my faith is small, Trust - ing Je - sus, that is all.
While He leads I can - not fall; Trust - ing Je - sus, that is all.
If in dan - ger, for Him call; Trust - ing Je - sus, that is all.
Till with - in the jas - per wall: Trust - ing Je - sus, that is all.

Chorus

Trust - ing as the mo - ments fly, Trust - ing as the days go by;

Trust - ing Him what-e'er be - fall, Trust - ing Je - sus, that is all.

229   Fall Fresh On Me

Arr. by B. B. McKinney

Spir - it of the liv - ing God, Fall fresh on me, Spir - it of the

D. S.—Spir - it of the

Fall Fresh On Me

FINE.

D. S.

liv-ing God, Fall fresh on me. Break me, melt me, mould me, fill me.

liv-ing God, Fall fresh on me.

230   The Light of the World Is Jesus

P. P. B.

P. P. BLISS

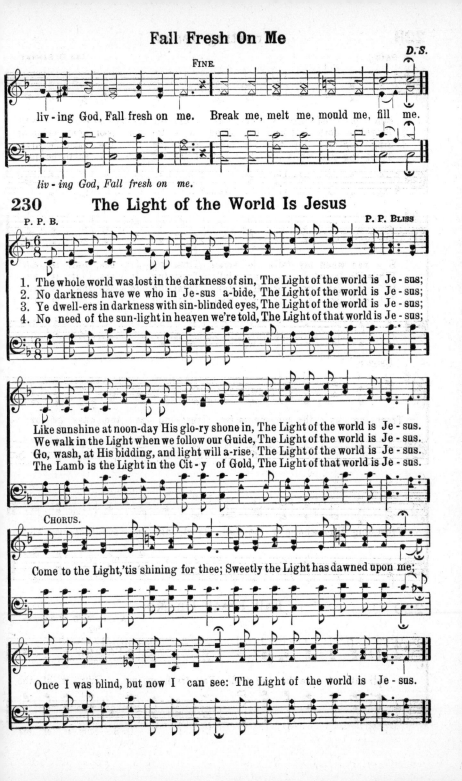

1. The whole world was lost in the darkness of sin, The Light of the world is Je-sus;
2. No darkness have we who in Je-sus a-bide, The Light of the world is Je-sus;
3. Ye dwell-ers in darkness with sin-blinded eyes, The Light of the world is Je-sus;
4. No need of the sun-light in heaven we're told, The Light of that world is Je-sus;

Like sunshine at noon-day His glo-ry shone in, The Light of the world is Je-sus.
We walk in the Light when we follow our Guide, The Light of the world is Je-sus.
Go, wash, at His bidding, and light will a-rise, The Light of the world is Je-sus.
The Lamb is the Light in the Cit-y of Gold, The Light of that world is Je-sus.

CHORUS.

Come to the Light, 'tis shining for thee; Sweetly the Light has dawned upon me;

Once I was blind, but now I can see: The Light of the world is Je-sus.

231 Revive Thy People, O Lord

ALBERT MIDLANE

B. B. McKINNEY

1. Re-vive Thy peo-ple, O Lord! Thy might-y arm make bare;
2. Re-vive Thy peo-ple, O Lord! Dis-turb this sleep of death;
3. Re-vive Thy peo-ple, O Lord! Cre-ate soul-thirst for Thee;
4. Re-vive Thy peo-ple, O Lord! Ex-alt Thy pre-cious name;

Speak with the voice that wakes the dead, And make Thy peo-ple hear.
Quick-en the smould'ring em-bers now By Thine Al-might-y breath.
But hun-g'ring for the bread of life, Oh, may our spir-its be.
And, by the Ho-ly Ghost, our love For Thee and Thine in-flame.

CHORUS from McGranahan

Re-vive! .... re-vive! .... And give re-fresh-ing show'rs; ...
Re-vive! re-vive! re-vive! re-vive! And give, oh, give re-fresh-ing show'rs;

The glo-ry shall be all Thine own; The bless-ing shall be ours.

Copyright, 1945, by Broadman Press

232 John Three Sixteen

JOHN 3: 16

B. B. McKINNEY

For God so loved the world, He gave His on-ly Son, That { Who-so-ev-er be-
{ Who-so-ev-er be-

Copyright, 1937, by The Sunday School Board of the Southern Baptist Convention

John Three Sixteen

liev-eth in Him,
liev-eth in Him, } Should not perish, should not perish, but have e-ter-nal life.

233 Take the Name of Jesus With You

Mrs. Lydia Baxter

W. H. Doane

1. Take the name of Je-sus with you, Child of sor-row and of woe—
2. Take the name of Je-sus ev-er, As a shield from ev-'ry snare;
3. O the pre-cious name of Je-sus! How it thrills our souls with joy,
4. At the name of Je-sus bow-ing, Fall-ing pros-trate at His feet,

It will joy and com-fort give you, Take it then wher-e'er you go.
If temp-ta-tions round you gath-er, Breathe that ho-ly name in prayer.
When His lov-ing arms re-ceive us, And His songs our tongues em-ploy!
King of kings in heav'n we'll crown Him, When our jour-ney is com-plete.

Chorus

Pre-cious name, O how sweet! Hope of earth and joy of heav'n;
Pre-cious name, O how sweet!

Pre-cious name, O how sweet! . . Hope of earth and joy of heav'n.
Pre-cious name, O how sweet, how sweet!

Follow the Living Christ

C. W. EVEREST, and B. B. McK.

B. B. McKINNEY

1. "Take up thy cross," the Sav-iour said, "Come and My dis-ci-ple be;
2. Take up thy cross, nor heed the shame, Bid thy fool-ish pride be still;
3. Take up thy cross with will-ing heart, Has-ten now thy life to yield;
4. Take up thy cross, and fol-low on, Nev-er seek to lay it down;

Take up thy cross, the world for-sake, And hum-bly fol-low aft-er Me."
The Lord went forth to die for thee Up-on a cross on Cal-vary's hill.
Go forth to serve the liv-ing Christ, And plant His cross in ev-ery field.
For on-ly he who bears the cross May hope to wear the glo-rious crown.

CHORUS

Fol - - low, fol - - low, Fol-low ev-ery day, Fol-low all the way;
Fol-low the Christ, fol-low the Christ;

rit.

Fol - - low, fol - - low, Fol-low the liv-ing Christ.
Fol-low the Christ, fol-low the Christ;

235 ## Saviour, More Than Life

FANNY J. CROSBY

W. H. DOANE

1. Sav-iour, more than life to me, I am cling-ing, cling-ing close to Thee;
2. Thro' this chang-ing world be-low, Lead me gen-tly, gen-tly as I go;
3. Let me love Thee more and more, Till this fleet-ing, fleet-ing life is o'er;

Saviour, More Than Life

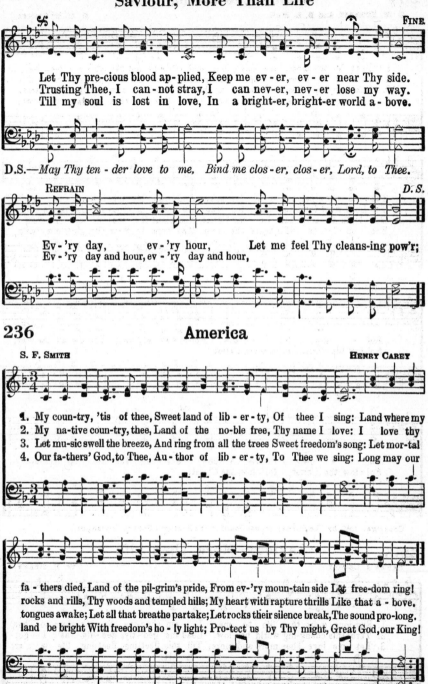

Let Thy pre-cious blood ap-plied, Keep me ev-er, ev-er near Thy side.
Trusting Thee, I can-not stray, I can nev-er, nev-er lose my way.
Till my soul is lost in love, In a bright-er, bright-er world a-bove.

D.S.—*May Thy ten-der love to me, Bind me clos-er, clos-er, Lord, to Thee.*

REFRAIN

Ev-'ry day, ev-'ry hour, Let me feel Thy cleans-ing pow'r;
Ev-'ry day and hour, ev-'ry day and hour,

236   America

S. F. SMITH   HENRY CAREY

1. My coun-try, 'tis of thee, Sweet land of lib-er-ty, Of thee I sing: Land where my
2. My na-tive coun-try, thee, Land of the no-ble free, Thy name I love: I love thy
3. Let mu-sic swell the breeze, And ring from all the trees Sweet freedom's song: Let mor-tal
4. Our fa-thers' God, to Thee, Au-thor of lib-er-ty, To Thee we sing: Long may our

fa-thers died, Land of the pil-grim's pride, From ev-'ry moun-tain side Let free-dom ring!
rocks and rills, Thy woods and templed hills; My heart with rapture thrills Like that a-bove.
tongues awake; Let all that breathe partake; Let rocks their silence break, The sound pro-long.
land be bright With freedom's ho-ly light; Pro-tect us by Thy might, Great God, our King!

237 Break Thou the Bread of Life

MARY ANN LATHBURY

WILLIAM F. SHERWIN

1. Break Thou the bread of life, Dear Lord, to me, As Thou didst
2. Bless Thou the truth, dear Lord, To me—to me— As Thou didst
3. Thou art the bread of life, O Lord, to me, Thy ho - ly
4. O send Thy Spir - it, Lord, Now un - to me, That He may

break the loaves Be - side the sea; Be - yond the sa - cred page
bless the bread By Gal - i - lee; Then shall all bond - age cease,
Word the truth That sav - eth me; Give me to eat and live
touch my eyes, And make me see: Show me the truth con-cealed

I seek Thee, Lord; My spir - it pants for Thee, O liv - ing Word.
All fet - ters fall; And I shall find my peace, My All in all.
With Thee a - bove; Teach me to love Thy truth, For Thou art love.
With - in Thy Word, And in Thy book re-vealed I see the Lord.

238 Lord, Lay Some Soul Upon My Heart

Anonymous

From EXCELL and SANKEY
Arr. B. B. McKINNEY

Lord, lay some soul up - on my heart, And love that soul thro' me.

Lord, Lay Some Soul Upon My Heart

And may I brave-ly do my part To win that soul for Thee.

239   Lead Me to Some Soul Today

In memory of D. L. Moody, who said: "I must speak to one soul each day about Christ"

WILL H. HOUGHTON   WENDELL P. LOVELESS

Lead me to some soul to-day, O teach me, Lord, just what to say;

Friends of mine are lost in sin, And can-not find their way.

Few there are who seem to care, And few there are who pray;
who pray;

Melt my heart and fill my life, Give me one soul to-day.

240 Child's Morning Hymn

REBECCA J. WESTON   D. BATCHELLOR

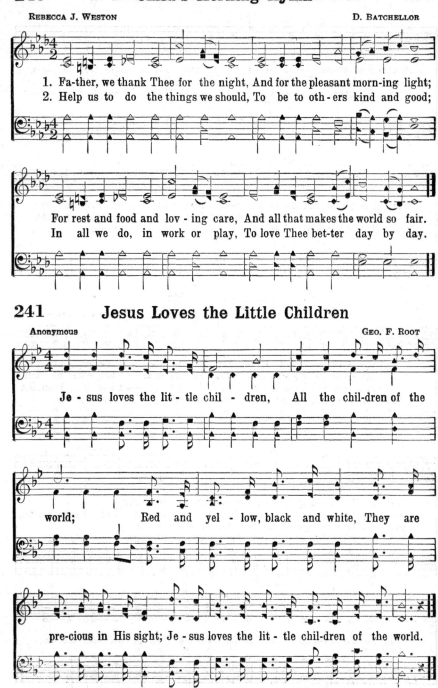

1. Fa-ther, we thank Thee for the night, And for the pleasant morn-ing light;
2. Help us to do the things we should, To be to oth-ers kind and good;

For rest and food and lov-ing care, And all that makes the world so fair.
In all we do, in work or play, To love Thee bet-ter day by day.

241   Jesus Loves the Little Children

Anonymous   GEO. F. ROOT

Je - sus loves the lit - tle chil - dren, All the chil-dren of the

world; Red and yel - low, black and white, They are

pre-cious in His sight; Je - sus loves the lit - tle chil-dren of the world.

Praise Him, All Ye Little Children

1. Praise Him, praise Him, all ye lit-tle chil-dren, God is love, God is love;
2. Love Him, love Him, all ye lit-tle chil-dren, God is love, God is love;
3. Thank Him, thank Him, all ye lit-tle chil-dren, God is love, God is love;

Praise Him, praise Him, all ye lit-tle chil-dren, God is love, God is love.
Love Him, love Him, all ye lit-tle chil-dren, God is love, God is love.
Thank Him, thank Him, all ye lit-tle chil-dren, God is love, God is love.

243

Jesus Loves Me

(The favorite Hymn of China)

WILLIAM B. BRADBURY

1. Je-sus loves me! this I know, For the Bi-ble tells me so; Lit-tle
2. Je-sus loves me! He who died Heav-en's gates to o-pen wide! He will
3. Je-sus loves me! loves me still, Tho' I'm ver-y weak and ill; From His
4. Je-sus loves me! He will stay Close be-side me all the way; If I

CHORUS

ones to Him be-long, They are weak, but He is strong.
wash a-way my sin, Let His lit-tle child come in. Yes, Je-sus loves me,
shining throne on high, Comes to watch me where I lie.
love Him when I die, He will take me home on high.

Yes, Je-sus loves me, Yes, Je-sus loves me, The Bi-ble tells me so.

244

Good Morning to You!

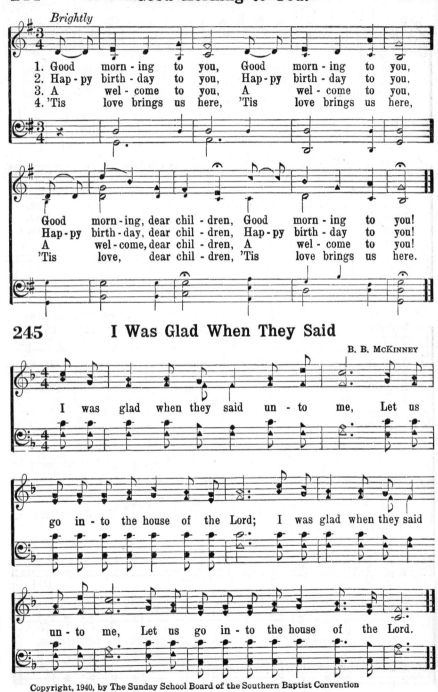

Brightly

1. Good morn-ing to you, Good morn-ing to you,
2. Hap-py birth-day to you, Hap-py birth-day to you,
3. A wel-come to you, A wel-come to you,
4. 'Tis love brings us here, 'Tis love brings us here,

Good morn-ing, dear chil-dren, Good morn-ing to you!
Hap-py birth-day, dear chil-dren, Hap-py birth-day to you!
A wel-come, dear chil-dren, A wel-come to you!
'Tis love, dear chil-dren, 'Tis love brings us here.

245

I Was Glad When They Said

B. B. McKinney

I was glad when they said un-to me, Let us

go in-to the house of the Lord; I was glad when they said

un-to me, Let us go in-to the house of the Lord.

246   **The Happy Story Hour**

AURORA M. SHUMATE   IDA T. TRUSS

In a happy manner

1. Ev - ery Sun-day eve - ning   To the Church we go
2. Here we have some sto - ries   Of God's love and care—
3. How we like the sing - ing   And the work and play!

For the hap-py Sto - ry Hour,   And we love it so.
Oth - ers tell us how to live   And with peo-ple share.
Hap - py, hap - py Sto - ry Hour—We can-not stay a - way.

CHORUS

The Sto - ry Hour, the Sto - ry Hour, The hap-py Sto - ry Hour,   We

sing and pray and lis - ten well, In the hap - py Sto - ry Hour.

247   **Prayer Response**

B. B. McKINNEY

Fa - ther, hear our prayer, We ask for Je - sus' sake.   A-MEN.

248

Count Your Blessings

Rev. Johnson Oatman, Jr.

E. O. Excell

1. When up-on life's bil-lows you are tem - pest-tossed, When you are dis-
2. Are you ev - er bur-dened with a load of care? Does the cross seem
3. When you look at oth - ers with their lands and gold, Think that Christ has
4. So, a - mid the con-flict, whether great or small, Do not be dis-

cour-aged, think-ing all is lost, Count your man-y bless-ings, name them
heav - y you are called to bear? Count your man-y bless-ings, ev - 'ry
prom-ised you His wealth un - told; Count your man-y bless-ings, mon-ey
cour-aged, God is o - ver all; Count your man-y bless-ings, an - gels

one by one, And it will sur-prise you what the Lord hath done.
doubt will fly, And you will be sing-ing as the days go by.
can - not buy Your re-ward in Heav-en, nor your home on high.
will at - tend, Help and com-fort give you to your jour - ney's end.

Chorus.

Count your bless-ings, Name them one by one; Count your
Count your man-y bless-ings, Name them one by one; Count your man-y

bless-ings, See what God hath done; Count your bless-ings,
bless-ings, See what God hath done; Count your man-y bless-ings,

Count Your Blessings

rit.   *a tempo*

Name them one by one; Count your man-y bless-ings, See what God hath done.

249   'Tis So Sweet to Trust in Jesus

LOUISA M. R. STEAD   WM. J. KIRKPATRICK

1. 'Tis so sweet to trust in Je-sus, Just to take Him at His Word;
2. O how sweet to trust in Je-sus, Just to trust His cleans-ing blood;
3. Yes, 'tis sweet to trust in Je-sus, Just from sin and self to cease;
4. I'm so glad I learned to trust Thee, Pre-cious Je-sus, Sav-ior, Friend;

Just to rest up-on His prom-ise; Just to know, "Thus saith the Lord."
Just in sim-ple faith to plunge me 'Neath the heal-ing, cleans-ing flood!
Just from Je-sus sim-ply tak-ing Life and rest, and joy and peace.
And I know that Thou art with me, Wilt be with me to the end.

CHORUS

Je-sus, Je-sus, how I trust Him! How I've proved Him o'er and o'er!

p

Je-sus, Je-sus, pre-cious Je-sus! O for grace to trust Him more!

C. H. G.

CHAS. H. GABRIEL

1. God is call-ing the prod-i-gal, come without de-lay, Hear, O hear Him
2. Pa - tient, lov-ing and ten-der-ly still the Fa-ther pleads, Hear, O hear Him
3. Come, there's bread in the house of thy Father, and to spare, Hear, O hear Him

call - ing, call - ing now for thee;   Tho' you've wandered so far from His
call - ing, call - ing now for thee;   Oh! re - turn while the Spir-it in
call - ing, call - ing now for thee;   Lo! the ta - ble is spread and the
for thee;

pres-ence, come to-day,   Hear His lov-ing voice call-ing still. . . . .
mer - cy in - ter - cedes,   Hear His lov-ing voice call-ing still.
feast is wait-ing there,   Hear His lov-ing voice call-ing still. (call-ing still.)

CHORUS

Call - - - ing now for thee, ... O wea - - - ry
Call-ing now for thee,   Call-ing now for thee,   Wea-ry prod-i-gal, come,

prod-i-gal, come; . . . .   Call - - - ing now for thee, ...
wea-ry prod-i-gal, come;   Call-ing now for thee,   Call-ing now for thee,

Calling the Prodigal

O wea - - - - ry prod-i-gal, come. . . . .
Wea - ry prod-i-gal, come,   wea - ry prod-i-gal, come.

251   **Bring Them In**

ALEXCENAH THOMAS   W. A. OGDEN

1. Hark! 'tis the Shepherd's voice I hear, Out in the des-ert dark and drear,
2. Who'll go and help this Shepherd kind, Help Him the wand'ring ones to find?
3. Out in the des-ert hear their cry, Out on the mountains wild and high;

Call - ing the sheep who've gone a-stray Far from the Shepherd's fold a-way.
Who'll bring the lost ones to the fold, Where they'll be sheltered from the cold?
Hark! 'tis the Mas-ter speaks to thee, "Go find my sheep wher-e'er they be."

CHORUS

Bring them in, bring them in, Bring them in from the fields of sin;

Bring them in, bring them in, Bring the wand'ring ones to Je - sus.

252 When the Roll is Called Up Yonder

J. M. B.   J. M. BLACK

1. When the trumpet of the Lord shall sound, and time shall be no more, And the
2. On that bright and cloudless morning when the dead in Christ shall rise, And the
3. Let us la-bor for the Mas-ter from the dawn till set-ting sun, Let us

morning breaks, e-ter-nal, bright and fair; When the saved of earth shall gather
glo-ry of His res-ur-rec-tion share; When His cho-sen ones shall gather
talk of all His wondrous love and care; Then when all of life is o-ver,

o-ver on the oth-er shore, And the roll is called up yon-der, I'll be there.
to their home beyond the skies, And the roll is called up yon-der, I'll be there.
and our work on earth is done, And the roll is called up yon-der, I'll be there.

CHORUS.

When the roll . . . . . . is called up yon - - - - der, When the
When the roll is called up yon-der, I'll be there,

roll . . . . is called up yon - - der, When the roll . . . . is called up
When the roll is called up yon-der, I'll be there,   When the roll is called up

When the Roll Is Called Up Yonder

yon - der, When the roll is called up yon - der, I'll be there.

253

Have Thine Own Way, Lord

ADELAIDE A. POLLARD

GEO. C. STEBBINS

Slowly

1. Have Thine own way, Lord! Have Thine own way!.. Thou art the
2. Have Thine own way, Lord! Have Thine own way!.. Search me and
3. Have Thine own way, Lord! Have Thine own way!.. Wound-ed and
4. Have Thine own way, Lord! Have Thine own way!.. Hold o'er my

Pot - ter; I am the clay... Mould me and make me Aft - er Thy
try me, Mas-ter, to - day!... Whit - er than snow, Lord, Wash me just
wea - ry, Help me, I pray!. Pow - er—all pow - er—Sure - ly is
be - ing Ab - so - lute sway!. Fill with Thy Spir - it Till all shall

will,... While I am wait - ing, Yield - ed and still...
now,... As in Thy pres - ence Hum - bly I bow...
Thine! Touch me and heal me, Sav - ior di - vine!..
see.... Christ on - ly, al - ways, Liv - ing in me!....

254 He Ransomed Me

Julia H. Johnston

J. W. Henderson

1. There's a sweet and bless-ed sto-ry Of the Christ who came from glo-ry,
2. From the depth of sin and sad-ness To the heights of joy and glad-ness
3. From the throne of heaven-ly glo-ry— Oh, the sweet and bless-ed sto-ry!
4. By and by with joy in-creas-ing, And with grat-i-tude un-ceas-ing,

Just to res-cue me from sin and mis-er-y; He in lov-ing-kindness sought me,
Je-sus lift-ed me, in mer-cy full and free; With His precious blood He bo't me,
Je-sus came to lift the lost in sin and woe In-to lib-er-ty all-glo-rious,
Lift-ed up with Christ for-ev-er-more to be; I will join the hosts there sing-ing,

ad lib.

And from sin and shame hath bro't me, Hal-le-lu-jah! Je-sus ran-somed me.
When I knew Him not, He sought me, And in love di-vine He ran-somed me.
Tro-phies of His grace vic-to-rious, Ev-er-more re-joic-ing here be-low.
In the an-them ev-er ring-ing, To the King of Love who ran-somed me.

CHORUS

Hal-le-lu-jah, what a Sav-iour! Who can take a poor lost sin-ner, Lift him

from the mir-y clay and set him free; (Hal-le-lu-jah!) I will ev-er tell the sto-ry,

He Ransomed Me

ad lib.

Shout-ing glo-ry, glo-ry, glo-ry, Hal-le-lu-jah! Je-sus ran-somed me.

255 Sweet Hour of Prayer

W. W. WALFORD

WM. B. BRADBURY

1. Sweet hour of prayer! sweet hour of prayer! That calls me from a world of care,
2. Sweet hour of prayer! sweet hour of prayer! Thy wings shall my pe-ti-tion bear
3. Sweet hour of prayer! sweet hour of prayer! May I thy con-so-la-tion share,

And bids me at my Father's throne Make all my wants and wish-es known;
To Him whose truth and faith-ful-ness En-gage the wait-ing soul to bless;
Till, from Mt. Pis-gah's loft-y height, I view my home, and take my flight:

In sea-sons of dis-tress and grief, My soul has oft-en found re-lief,
And since He bids me seek His face, Be-lieve His word and trust His grace,
This robe of flesh I'll drop, and rise To seize the ev-er-last-ing prize;

And oft es-caped the tempter's snare By thy re-turn, sweet hour of prayer.
I'll cast on Him my ev-'ry care, And wait for thee, sweet hour of prayer.
And shout, while passing thro' the air, Farewell, farewell, sweet hour of prayer.

256 I Shall Not Live in Vain

B. B. McK.

B. B. McKinney.

1. If I can plant a rose where thorns have been, Dis-pel the gloom, and let the sun-shine in; If I can help some bro-ken life to rise a-gain, I shall not live in vain, . . I shall not live . . in vain.

2. If I can sing a song of love and cheer, Some song that lifts a soul from doubt and fear, And bring them back to know that God is al-ways near, I shall not live in vain, . . I shall not live . . in vain.

3. If I can be a light wher-e'er I go, A light to shine for those in sin and woe, If I can lead some soul my liv-ing Christ to know, I shall not live in vain, . . I shall not live . . in vain.

257 The Rainbow With the Rain

B. B. McK.

B. B. McKinney.

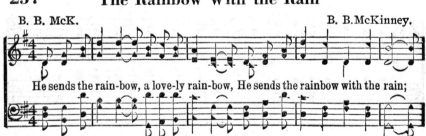

He sends the rain-bow, a love-ly rain-bow, He sends the rainbow with the rain;

The Rainbow With the Rain

He sends the sun-shine up-on the shad-ow, He sends the rainbow with the rain.

258

Trust, Try and Prove Me

L. S. L.

Lida Shivers Leech.

1. Bring ye all the tithes in-to the storehouse, All your money, talents, time and love;
2. When my wav'ring faith in trials fal-ter, When His guiding hand I can-not see,
3. I have yield-ed Him my life for-ev-er, All I am, or have, or hope to be;

Con - se-crate them all up-on the al-tar; While your Sav-ior from a-
Then in won-drous love and ten-der mer-cy, Thro' His word He says to
Naught on earth my hold on Him can sev-er, While I hear Him say to

rit. REFRAIN.

bove speaks sweet-ly, Trust Me, try Me, prove Me, saith the Lord of
me, My child, just
me, My child, just Trust Me, yes, then try Me, prove Me,

hosts and see If a bless-ing, unmeasured bless-ing, I will not pour out on Thee.

259

Golden Palaces

B. B. McK.
DUET

B. B. McKinney

1. Out of the gold-en pal-a-ces Je-sus, the Sav-iour came,
2. Out of the gold-en pal-a-ces, Out of a sun-lit sky,
3. Out of the gold-en pal-a-ces Je-sus will come a-gain

In-to an aw-ful world of woe, Lost in its sin and shame.
Je-sus came forth to bear His cross,—On Cal-v'ry's hill to die.
In all His glo-rious maj-es-ty, With His re-deemed to reign.

CHORUS

Out of the gold-en pal-a-ces, Out from His roy-al throne (His throne),

Je-sus the Lamb came forth to die, That He might save His own.

260

Thy Holy Temple

JOHN WILLIAM LOWE

B. B. McKINNEY, Jr.

1. This is Thy ho-ly tem-ple, Lord, Our sa-cred house of prayer.
2. Here, Fa-ther, we would wor-ship Thee, The Sav-iour of our soul;
3. We lis-ten to Thy sa-cred Word, And turn our hearts to prayer;
4. Be-hold the la-bor of our hands— Our of-fer-ing we give;

Thy Holy Temple

Our peo-ple meet with one ac-cord, And leave with Thee their care.
Since Thou hast ful-ly set us free, Re-deemed, we are made whole.
His message comes from Christ our Lord, And saves men from de-spair.
And send Thy Word to dis-tant lands, That all may hear and live. A-MEN.

261 My Jesus, I Love Thee

Author Unknown

A. J. GORDON

1. My Je-sus, I love Thee, I know Thou art mine, For Thee all the
2. I love Thee, be-cause Thou hast first lov-ed me, And pur-chased my
3. I'll love Thee in life, I will love Thee in death, And praise Thee as
4. In man-sions of glo-ry and end-less de-light, I'll ev-er a-

fol-lies of sin I re-sign; My gra-cious Re-deem-er, my
par-don on Cal-va-ry's tree; I love Thee for wear-ing the
long as Thou lend-est me breath; And say when the death-dew lies
dore Thee in heav-en so bright; I'll sing with the glit-ter-ing

Sav-iour art Thou; If ev-er I loved Thee, my Je-sus, 'tis now.
thorns on Thy brow: If ev-er I loved Thee, my Je-sus, 'tis now.
cold on my brow, If ev-er I loved Thee, my Je-sus, 'tis now.
crown on my brow, If ev-er I loved Thee, my Je-sus, 'tis now.

Beneath the Cross of Jesus

Elizabeth C. Clephane   ST. CHRISTOPHER   Frederick C. Maker

1. Be - neath the cross of Je - sus I fain would take my stand,
2. Up - on that cross of Je - sus Mine eye at times can see
3. I take, O cross, thy shad - ow For my a - bid - ing place;

The shad - ow of a might - y Rock With - in a wea - ry land;
The ver - y dy - ing form of One Who suf - fered there for me;
I ask no oth - er sun-shine than The sun - shine of His face;

A home with-in the wil - der - ness, A rest up - on the way,
And from my smit-ten heart with tears, Two won - ders I con - fess,—
Con - tent to let the world go by, To know no gain nor loss,

From the burn-ing of the noon-tide heat, And the bur-den of the day.
The won-ders of His glo-rious love And my own worth-less-ness.
My sin - ful self my on - ly shame, My glo - ry all the cross!

263 Softly Now the Light of Day

Geo. W. Doane   SEYMOUR   Carl M. von Weber

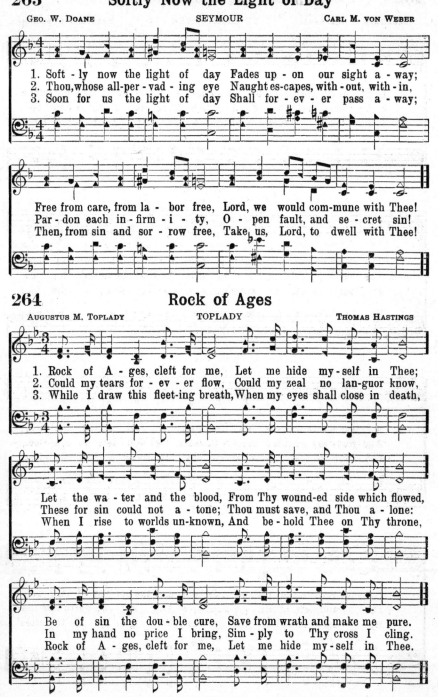

1. Soft - ly now the light of day Fades up - on our sight a - way;
2. Thou, whose all - per - vad - ing eye Naught es - capes, with - out, with - in,
3. Soon for us the light of day Shall for - ev - er pass a - way;

Free from care, from la - bor free, Lord, we would com - mune with Thee!
Par - don each in - firm - i - ty, O - pen fault, and se - cret sin!
Then, from sin and sor - row free, Take us, Lord, to dwell with Thee!

264 Rock of Ages

Augustus M. Toplady   TOPLADY   Thomas Hastings

1. Rock of A - ges, cleft for me, Let me hide my - self in Thee;
2. Could my tears for - ev - er flow, Could my zeal no lan-guor know,
3. While I draw this fleet-ing breath, When my eyes shall close in death,

Let the wa - ter and the blood, From Thy wound-ed side which flowed,
These for sin could not a - tone; Thou must save, and Thou a - lone:
When I rise to worlds un-known, And be - hold Thee on Thy throne,

Be of sin the dou - ble cure, Save from wrath and make me pure.
In my hand no price I bring, Sim - ply to Thy cross I cling.
Rock of A - ges, cleft for me, Let me hide my - self in Thee.

Let the Lower Lights Be Burning

P. P. B.

P. P. Bliss

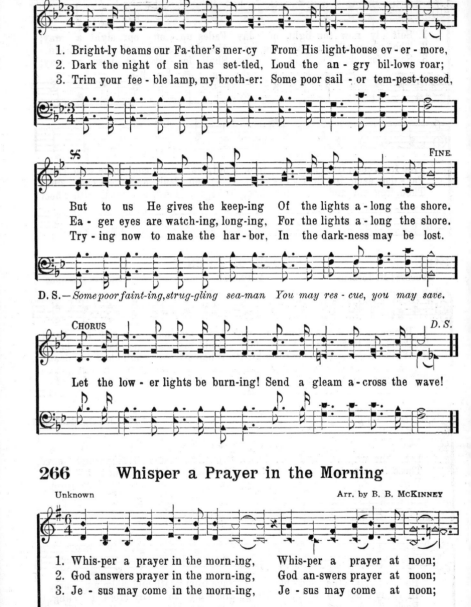

1. Bright-ly beams our Fa-ther's mer-cy From His light-house ev-er-more,
2. Dark the night of sin has set-tled, Loud the an-gry bil-lows roar;
3. Trim your fee-ble lamp, my broth-er: Some poor sail-or tem-pest-tossed,

But to us He gives the keep-ing Of the lights a-long the shore.
Ea-ger eyes are watch-ing, long-ing, For the lights a-long the shore.
Try-ing now to make the har-bor, In the dark-ness may be lost.

D. S.—*Some poor faint-ing, strug-gling sea-man You may res-cue, you may save.*

CHORUS

Let the low-er lights be burn-ing! Send a gleam a-cross the wave!

266

Whisper a Prayer in the Morning

Unknown

Arr. by B. B. McKinney

1. Whis-per a prayer in the morn-ing, Whis-per a prayer at noon;
2. God answers prayer in the morn-ing, God an-swers prayer at noon;
3. Je-sus may come in the morn-ing, Je-sus may come at noon;

Whisper a Prayer in the Morning

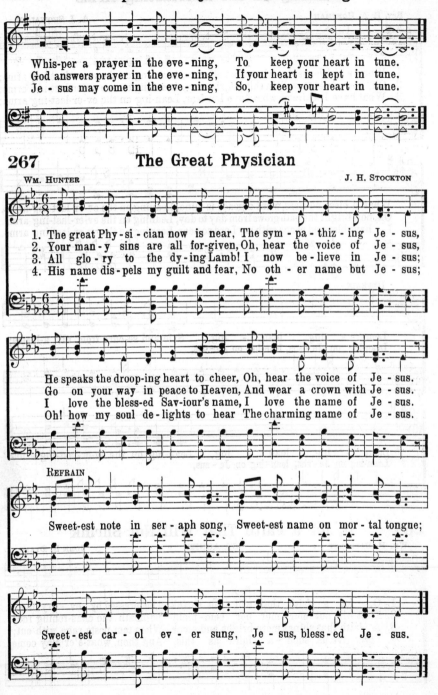

Whis-per a prayer in the eve - ning, To keep your heart in tune.
God answers prayer in the eve - ning, If your heart is kept in tune.
Je - sus may come in the eve - ning, So, keep your heart in tune.

267 The Great Physician

WM. HUNTER

J. H. STOCKTON

1. The great Phy - si - cian now is near, The sym - pa - thiz - ing Je - sus,
2. Your man - y sins are all for-given, Oh, hear the voice of Je - sus,
3. All glo - ry to the dy - ing Lamb! I now be - lieve in Je - sus;
4. His name dis - pels my guilt and fear, No oth - er name but Je - sus;

He speaks the droop-ing heart to cheer, Oh, hear the voice of Je - sus.
Go on your way in peace to Heaven, And wear a crown with Je - sus.
I love the bless-ed Sav-iour's name, I love the name of Je - sus.
Oh! how my soul de - lights to hear The charming name of Je - sus.

REFRAIN

Sweet-est note in ser - aph song, Sweet-est name on mor - tal tongue;

Sweet-est car - ol ev - er sung, Je - sus, bless - ed Je - sus.

Leaning On the Everlasting Arms

Rev. E. A. Hoffman

A. J. Showalter

1. What a fel-low-ship, what a joy di-vine, Lean-ing on the ev-er-last-ing arms;
2. Oh, how sweet to walk in this pilgrim way, Lean-ing on the ev-er-last-ing arms;
3. What have I to dread, what have I to fear, Lean-ing on the ev-er-last-ing arms;

What a bless-ed-ness, what a peace is mine, Leaning on the ev-er-last-ing arms.
Oh, how bright the path grows from day to day, Leaning on the ev-er-last-ing arms.
I have bless-ed peace with my Lord so near, Leaning on the ev-er-last-ing arms.

Refrain

Lean - ing, lean - ing, Safe and se-cure from all a-larms;
Lean-ing on Je - sus, lean-ing on Je-sus,

Lean - ing, lean - ing, Lean-ing on the ev-er-last-ing arms.
Lean-ing on Je - sus, lean-ing on Je - sus,

269 O, for a Faith That Will Not Shrink

Wm. H. Bathurst

ST. AGNES

John B. Dykes

1. O, for a faith that will not shrink, Tho' pressed by ev - ery foe,
2. That will not mur - mur nor com - plain Be-neath the chas-tening rod,
3. A faith that shines more bright and clear When tem-pests rage with-out;
4. Lord, give us such a faith as this, And then, what-e'er may come,

O, for a Faith That Will Not Shrink

That will not trem-ble on the brink Of an-y earth-ly woe!—
But, in the hour of grief or pain, Will lean up-on its God;—
That when in dan-ger knows no fear, In dark-ness feels no doubt.—
We'll taste, e'en here, the hal-lowed bliss Of an e-ter-nal home.

270 There Is a Name I Love to Hear

1. There is a name I love to hear, I love to sing its worth; It sounds like
2. It tells me of a Sav-iour's love, Who died to set me free; It tells me
3. It tells me what my Fa-ther hath In store for ev-er-y day, And tho' I
4. It tells of One whose loving heart Can feel my deep-est woe, Who in each

mu-sic in mine ear, The sweet-est name on earth.
of His precious blood, The sin-ner's per-fect plea. Oh, how I love Je-sus,
tread a darksome path, Yields sunshine all the way.
sor-row bears a part, That none can bear be-low.

CHORUS

Oh, how I love Je-sus, Oh, how I love Je-sus, Be-cause He first loved me.

271 I Am Praying for You

S. O'Maley Cluff

Ira D. Sankey

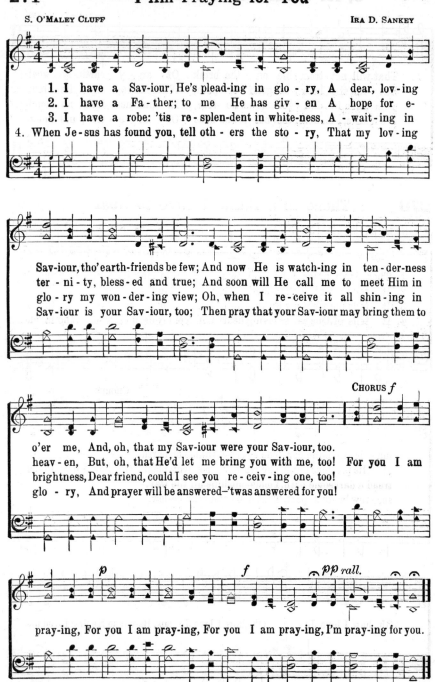

1. I have a Sav-iour, He's plead-ing in glo-ry, A dear, lov-ing
2. I have a Fa-ther; to me He has giv-en A hope for e-
3. I have a robe: 'tis re-splen-dent in white-ness, A-wait-ing in
4. When Je-sus has found you, tell oth-ers the sto-ry, That my lov-ing

Sav-iour, tho' earth-friends be few; And now He is watch-ing in ten-der-ness
ter-ni-ty, bless-ed and true; And soon will He call me to meet Him in
glo-ry my won-der-ing view; Oh, when I re-ceive it all shin-ing in
Sav-iour is your Sav-iour, too; Then pray that your Sav-iour may bring them to

CHORUS *f*

o'er me, And, oh, that my Sav-iour were your Sav-iour, too.
heav-en, But, oh, that He'd let me bring you with me, too! **For you I am**
brightness, Dear friend, could I see you re-ceiv-ing one, too!
glo-ry, And prayer will be answered—'twas answered for you!

p   *f*   *pp rall.*

pray-ing, For you I am pray-ing, For you I am pray-ing, I'm pray-ing for you.

272 The Haven of Rest

H. L. Gilmour

George D. Moore

1. My soul in sad ex - ile was out on life's sea, So bur-dened with
2. I yield - ed my-self to His ten - der em - brace, And, faith tak-ing
3. The song of my soul, since the Lord made me whole, Has been the old
4. Oh, come to the Sav - iour, He pa - tient-ly waits, To save by His

sin and dis - trest, Till I heard a sweet voice say-ing, "Make Me your choice,"
hold of the word, My fet - ters fell off, and I an-chored my soul:
sto - ry so blest, Of Je - sus, who'll save who-so - ev - er will have
pow - er di - vine; Come, an-chor your soul in the ha - ven of rest,

D. S.—*The tem-pest may sweep o'er the wild storm - y deep,*

FINE CHORUS

And I en - tered the ha - ven of rest.
The ha - ven of rest is my Lord. **I've an-chored my**
A home in the ha - ven of rest.
And say, "My Be - lov - ed is mine."

In Je - sus I'm safe ev - er - more.

D. S.

soul in the ha - ven of rest, I'll sail the wild seas no more;

Jesus Loves Even Me

P. P. B.

P. P. Bliss

1. I am so glad that our Fa - ther in heaven Tells of His
2. Tho' I for - get Him and wan - der a - way, Still He doth
3. Oh, if there's on - ly one song I can sing, When in His

love in the Book He has given; Won - der - ful things in the
love me wher - ev - er I stray; Back to His dear lov - ing
beau - ty I see the great King, This shall my song in e -

Bi - ble I see: This is the dear - est, that Je - sus loves me.
arms would I flee, When I re - mem - ber that Je - sus loves me.
ter - ni - ty be: "Oh, what a won - der that Je - sus loves me."

CHORUS

I am so glad that Je - sus loves me, Je - sus loves me, Je - sus loves me,

I am so glad that Je - sus loves me, Je - sus loves e - ven me.

I Will Not Forget Thee

C. H. G.

CHAS. H. GABRIEL

1. Sweet is the prom-ise—"I will not for-get thee," Noth-ing can mo-lest or
2. Trusting the prom-ise—"I will not for-get thee," On-ward will I go with
3. When at the gold-en por-tals I am stand-ing, All my trib-u-la-tions,

turn my soul a-way; E'en tho' the night be dark with-in the val-ley,
songs of joy and love; Tho' earth de-spise me, tho' my friends for-sake me,
all my sor-rows past, How sweet to hear the bless-ed proc-la-ma-tion,

CHORUS

Just be-yond is shin-ing one e-ter-nal day. I .... will not for-get thee or
I shall be re-mem-bered in my home a-bove.
"En-ter, faithful servant, welcome home at last!" I will not for-get thee, I will nev-er

leave thee; In My hands I'll hold thee, in My arms I'll fold thee; I .... will
leave thee; I will not for-get

not for-get thee or leave thee; I am thy Re-deem-er, I will care for thee.
thee, for-get

275 Breathe On Me

EDWIN HATCH   B. B. McKINNEY

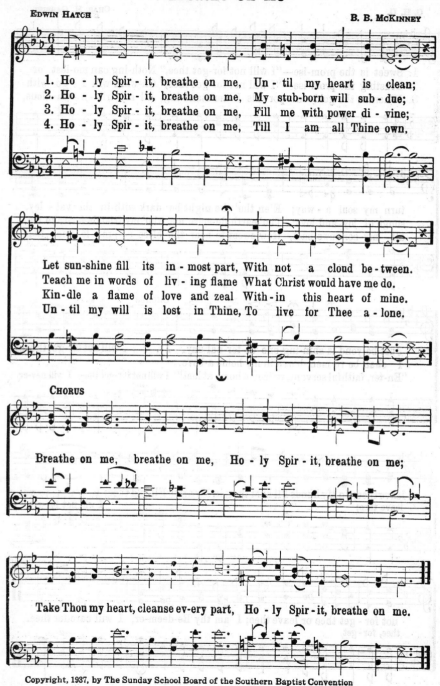

1. Ho - ly Spir - it, breathe on me, Un - til my heart is clean;
2. Ho - ly Spir - it, breathe on me, My stub-born will sub - due;
3. Ho - ly Spir - it, breathe on me, Fill me with power di - vine;
4. Ho - ly Spir - it, breathe on me, Till I am all Thine own,

Let sun-shine fill its in - most part, With not a cloud be - tween.
Teach me in words of liv - ing flame What Christ would have me do.
Kin-dle a flame of love and zeal With-in this heart of mine.
Un - til my will is lost in Thine, To live for Thee a - lone.

CHORUS

Breathe on me, breathe on me, Ho - ly Spir - it, breathe on me;

Take Thou my heart, cleanse ev-ery part, Ho - ly Spir - it, breathe on me.

276 Have I Grieved Thy Holy Spirit?

Rev. Oswald J. Smith.

B. D. Ackley.

1. Have I grieved Thy Ho-ly Spir - it? Have I quenched His pow'r within?
2. Do I lack the grace He giv-eth? Have I pow'r to win the lost?
3. Do I yield to sin's al-lure - ment, Hav - ing lost the pow'r to win,
4. Lord, I come in deep con-tri - tion, Yield-ing all I have to Thee,

If I have, O Lord, for-give me, Cleanse my heart from ev'ry sin. . . .
Is my message un-a-vail - ing? Give Him back at an-y cost! . . .
Since Thy Spirit, grieved, forsook me, When I let the tempter in? . . .
Mak - ing now a full sur-ren - der— Thine for-ev-er would I be. . . .

CHORUS

O my Savior, come, I pray Thee, As I at Thine altar bow; . . . .

Hear, O hear my heart's con-fes-sion, Par - don, cleanse, and fill me now.

277 In the Garden

C. A. M.

C. Austin Miles

1. I come to the gar-den a-lone, While the dew is still on the
2. He speaks, and the sound of His voice Is so sweet the birds hush their
3. I'd stay in the gar-den with Him Though the night a-round me be

ros - es, And the voice I hear, Fall-ing on my ear, The
sing - ing, And the mel - o - dy That He gave to me, With-
fall - ing, But He bids me go; Thro' the voice of woe His

CHORUS

Son of God dis-clos - es.
in my heart is ring - ing. And He walks with me, and He
voice to me is call - ing.

talks with me, And He tells me I am His own; And the

joy we share as we tar - ry there, None oth-er has ev-er known.

278 By the Way of the Cross

B. B. McK.

B. B. McKinney

1. On a hill lone and gray, In a land far a-way, Je-sus died in His
2. To the cross we must go, With our sin and its woe, We must tread where the
3. Look to Christ wea-ry soul, He can save and make whole, Turn a-way from your

an-guish and loss; There a-tone-ment was made, And the sin-debt was paid,
Mas-ter hath trod, If with Him we shall stand On that bright golden strand,
sin and its dross; He a-lone died for thee, Trust in Him and be free,

Chorus

Je-sus saves by the way of the cross.
In that beau-ti-ful cit-y of God. By the way of the cross,
Je-sus saves by the way of the cross.

"The old rug-ged cross" Je-sus saves by the way of the cross; His a-
the cross;

tone-ment a-lone Leads to heav'n and home Je-sus saves by the way of the cross.

Sunlight

J. W. Van DeVenter

W. S. Weeden

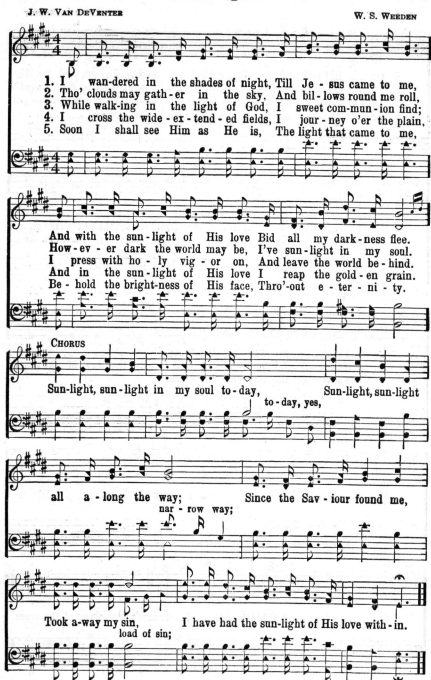

1. I wan-dered in the shades of night, Till Je-sus came to me,
2. Tho' clouds may gath-er in the sky, And bil-lows round me roll,
3. While walk-ing in the light of God, I sweet com-mun-ion find;
4. I cross the wide - ex - tend - ed fields, I jour - ney o'er the plain,
5. Soon I shall see Him as He is, The light that came to me,

And with the sun - light of His love Bid all my dark - ness flee.
How - ev - er dark the world may be, I've sun - light in my soul.
I press with ho - ly vig - or on, And leave the world be - hind.
And in the sun - light of His love I reap the gold - en grain.
Be - hold the bright - ness of His face, Thro' - out e - ter - ni - ty.

CHORUS

Sun-light, sun-light in my soul to-day, Sun-light, sun-light
to-day, yes,

all a - long the way; Since the Sav - iour found me,
nar - row way;

Took a-way my sin, I have had the sun-light of His love with - in.
load of sin;

280 I Will Sing the Wondrous Story

F. H. Rowley   Peter P. Bilhorn

1. I will sing the won-drous sto - ry Of the Christ who died for me,
2. I was lost, but Je - sus found me, Found the sheep that went a - stray,
3. I was bruised, but Je - sus healed me; Faint was I from man-y a fall;
4. Days of dark-ness still come o'er me, Sor-row's paths I of - ten tread,
5. He will keep me till the riv - er Rolls its wa - ters at my feet;

How He left His home in glo - ry For the cross of Cal - va - ry.
Threw His lov - ing arms a - round me, Drew me back in - to His way.
Sight was gone, and fears pos-sessed me, But He freed me from them all.
But the Sav - iour still is with me; By His hand I'm safe - ly led.
Then He'll bear me safe - ly o - ver, Where the loved ones I shall meet.

CHORUS

Yes, I'll sing .... the won-drous sto - ry Of the
Yes, I'll sing   the won-drous sto - ry

Christ ... who died for me, ... Sing it with .... the saints in
Of the Christ   who died for me,   Sing it with

glo - - ry, Gath-ered by .... the crys-tal sea.
the saints in glo - ry,   Gath-ered by   the crys-tal sea.

281 Bringing In the Sheaves

KNOWLES SHAW

GEORGE A. MINOR

1. Sow-ing in the morn-ing, sow-ing seeds of kind-ness, Sowing in the
2. Sow-ing in the sun-shine, sow-ing in the shad-ows, Fear-ing nei-ther
3. Go-ing forth with weep-ing, sow-ing for the Mas-ter, Tho' the loss sus-

noon-tide and the dew-y eve; Wait-ing for the har-vest,
clouds nor win-ter's chill-ing breeze; By and by the har-vest
tained our spir-it of-ten grieves; When our weep-ing's o-ver,

and the time of reap-ing, We shall come re-joic-ing, bring-ing in the sheaves.
and the la-bor end-ed, We shall come re-joic-ing, bring-ing in the sheaves.
He will bid us wel-come, We shall come re-joic-ing, bring-ing in the sheaves.

CHORUS

Bring-ing in the sheaves, bring-ing in the sheaves, We shall come re-joic-
Bring-ing in the sheaves, bring-ing in the sheaves, We shall come re-joic-

1
ing, bring-ing in the sheaves;

2
ing, bring-ing in the sheaves.

I Would Be Like Thee

B. B. McK.

B. B. McKinney

1. I would be like Thee, Beau-ti-ful Sav-iour, This is my heart-cry,
2. I would be like Thee, Won-der-ful Sav-iour, Gen-tle in spir-it,
3. I would be like Thee, Bless-ed Re-deem-er, Seek-ing poor sin-ners

this is my plea; Search me and try me, cleanse me and heal me,
lov-ing and kind; Cheer-ing the lone-ly, feed-ing the help-less,
lost in the night; May Thy com-pas-sion ev-er pos-sess me,

Chorus

That I may walk each moment with Thee.
Lift-ing the fall-en, lead-ing the blind.   I would be like Thee, Wonderful
That I might lead them in-to the light.

Sav-iour, In-to Thy hands my all I re-sign; Take me and

mold me, fill me and use me Now and for-ev-er I shall be Thine.

283 On Jordan's Stormy Banks

Samuel Stennett

Arr. by R. M. McIntosh

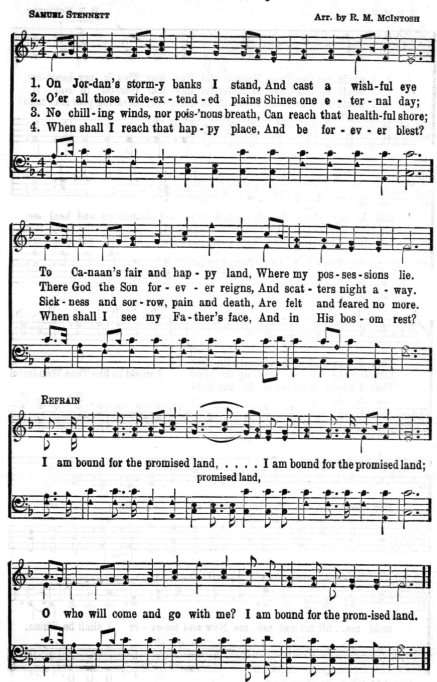

1. On Jor-dan's storm-y banks I stand, And cast a wish-ful eye
2. O'er all those wide-ex-tend-ed plains Shines one e-ter-nal day;
3. No chill-ing winds, nor pois-'nous breath, Can reach that health-ful shore;
4. When shall I reach that hap-py place, And be for-ev-er blest?

To Ca-naan's fair and hap-py land, Where my pos-ses-sions lie.
There God the Son for-ev-er reigns, And scat-ters night a-way.
Sick-ness and sor-row, pain and death, Are felt and feared no more.
When shall I see my Fa-ther's face, And in His bos-om rest?

Refrain

I am bound for the promised land, ... I am bound for the promised land;
promised land,

O who will come and go with me? I am bound for the prom-ised land.

284 Let Others See Jesus in You

B. B. McK.   B. B. McKinney

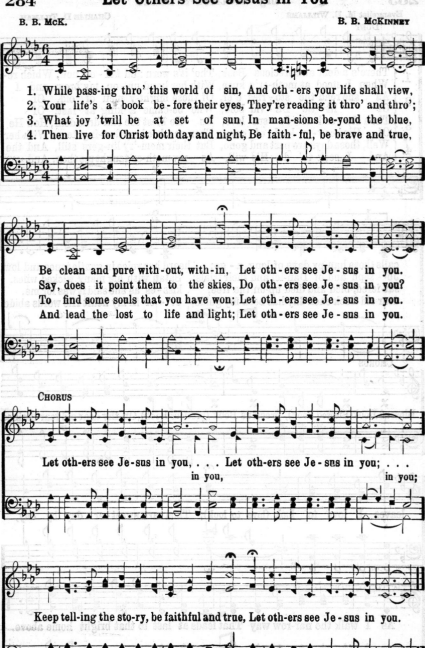

1. While pass-ing thro' this world of sin, And oth-ers your life shall view,
2. Your life's a book be-fore their eyes, They're reading it thro' and thro';
3. What joy 'twill be at set of sun, In man-sions be-yond the blue,
4. Then live for Christ both day and night, Be faith-ful, be brave and true,

Be clean and pure with-out, with-in, Let oth-ers see Je-sus in you.
Say, does it point them to the skies, Do oth-ers see Je-sus in you?
To find some souls that you have won; Let oth-ers see Je-sus in you.
And lead the lost to life and light; Let oth-ers see Je-sus in you.

CHORUS

Let oth-ers see Je-sus in you, . . . Let oth-ers see Je-sus in you; . . .
in you,   in you;

Keep tell-ing the sto-ry, be faithful and true, Let oth-ers see Je-sus in you.

285 My Mother's Bible

Evangelist M. B. WILLIAMS   CHARLIE D. TILLMAN

DUET

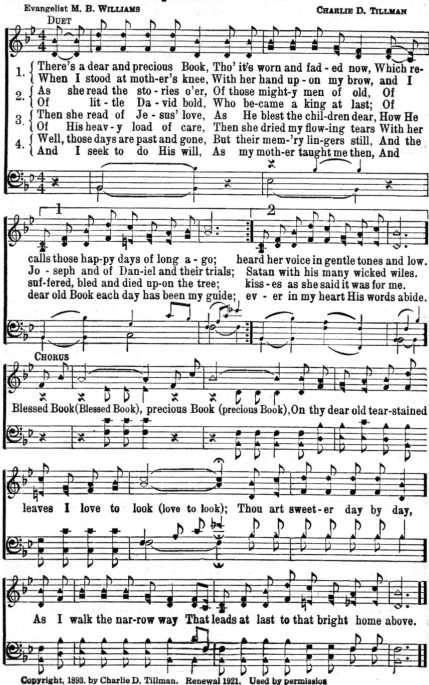

1. There's a dear and precious Book, Tho' it's worn and fad-ed now, Which re-
   When I stood at moth-er's knee, With her hand up-on my brow, and I

2. As she read the sto-ries o'er, Of those might-y men of old, Of
   Of lit-tle Da-vid bold, Who be-came a king at last; Of

3. Then she read of Je-sus' love, As He blest the chil-dren dear, How He
   Of His heav-y load of care, Then she dried my flow-ing tears With her

4. Well, those days are past and gone, But their mem-'ry lin-gers still, And the
   And I seek to do His will, As my moth-er taught me then, And

1. calls those hap-py days of long a-go;
   Jo-seph and of Dan-iel and their trials;
   suf-fered, bled and died up-on the tree;
   dear old Book each day has been my guide;

2. heard her voice in gentle tones and low.
   Satan with his many wicked wiles.
   kiss-es as she said it was for me.
   ev-er in my heart His words abide.

CHORUS

Blessed Book (Blessed Book), precious Book (precious Book), On thy dear old tear-stained

leaves I love to look (love to look); Thou art sweet-er day by day,

As I walk the nar-row way That leads at last to that bright home above.

286 Give of Your Best to the Master

H. B. G.   BARNARD   Mrs. Charles Barnard

1. Give of your best to the Mas-ter; Give of the strength of your youth;
2. Give of your best to the Mas-ter; Give Him first place in your heart;
3. Give of your best to the Mas-ter; Naught else is wor-thy His love;

REF.—*Give of your best to the Mas-ter; Give of the strength of your youth;*

FINE

Throw your soul's fresh, glowing ar - dor   In - to the bat-tle for truth.
Give Him first place in your serv-ice,   Con-se-crate ev - ery part.
He gave Him-self for your ran-som,   Gave up His glo-ry a-bove:

Clad in sal - va-tion's full ar - mor, Join in the bat-tle for truth.

Je - sus has set the ex - am - ple; Dauntless was He, young and brave;
Give, and to you shall be giv - en; God His be - lov - ed Son gave;
Laid down His life with-out mur - mur, You from sin's ru - in to save;

rall.   D. C. Ref.

Give Him your loy - al de - vo - tion, Give Him the best that you have. . .
Grate-ful - ly seek-ing to serve Him, Give Him the best that you have. . .
Give Him your heart's ad-o - ra - tion, Give Him the best that you have. . .

Zion Stands with Hills Surrounded

Thomas Kelly   Dr. Thos. Hastings

1. Zi - on stands with hills sur-round-ed—Zi - on, kept by power di - vine;
2. Ev - ery hu - man tie may per - ish; Friend to friend un-faith-ful prove;
3. In the fur - nace God may prove thee, Thence to bring thee forth more bright,

All her foes shall be con-found-ed, Though the world in arms com - bine:
Moth-ers cease their own to cher - ish; Heaven and earth at last re - move;
But can nev - er cease to love thee: Thou art pre-cious in His sight:

Hap - py Zi - on, What a fa - vored lot is thine!
But no chang - es Can at - tend Je - ho - vah's love;
God is with thee,—God, thine ev - er - last - ing light;

Hap - py Zi - on, What a fa - vored lot is thine!
But no chang - es Can at - tend Je - ho - vah's love.
God is with thee,—God, thine ev - er - last - ing light.

288 In Thy Holy Temple

B. B. McKinney, Sr. B. B. McKinney, Jr.

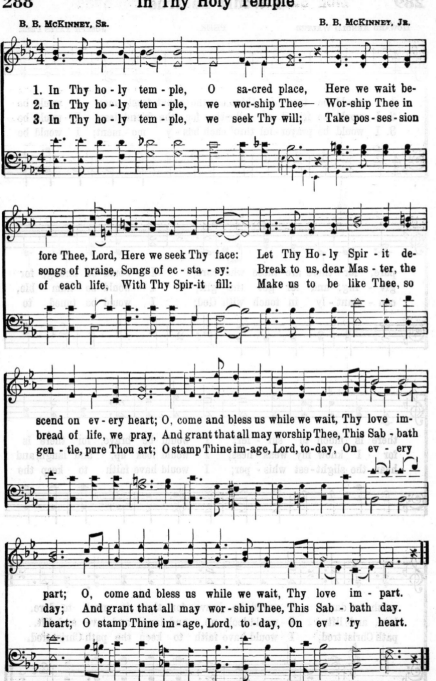

1. In Thy ho-ly tem-ple, O sa-cred place, Here we wait be-
2. In Thy ho-ly tem-ple, we wor-ship Thee— Wor-ship Thee in
3. In Thy ho-ly tem-ple, we seek Thy will; Take pos-ses-sion

fore Thee, Lord, Here we seek Thy face: Let Thy Ho-ly Spir-it de-
songs of praise, Songs of ec-sta-sy: Break to us, dear Mas-ter, the
of each life, With Thy Spir-it fill: Make us to be like Thee, so

scend on ev-ery heart; O, come and bless us while we wait, Thy love im-
bread of life, we pray, And grant that all may worship Thee, This Sab-bath
gen-tle, pure Thou art; O stamp Thine im-age, Lord, to-day, On ev-ery

part; O, come and bless us while we wait, Thy love im-part.
day; And grant that all may wor-ship Thee, This Sab-bath day.
heart; O stamp Thine im-age, Lord, to-day, On ev-'ry heart.

289 I Would Be True

HOWARD ARNOLD WALTER   PEEK   JOSEPH YATES PEEK

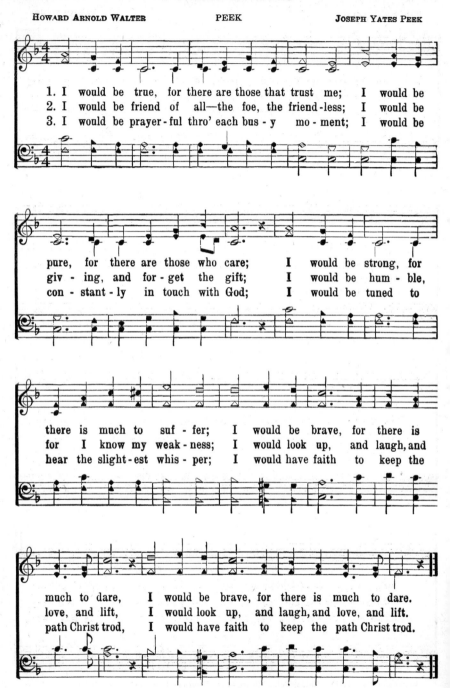

1. I would be true, for there are those that trust me; I would be
2. I would be friend of all—the foe, the friend-less; I would be
3. I would be prayer-ful thro' each bus-y mo-ment; I would be

pure, for there are those who care; I would be strong, for
giv-ing, and for-get the gift; I would be hum-ble,
con-stant-ly in touch with God; I would be tuned to

there is much to suf-fer; I would be brave, for there is
for I know my weak-ness; I would look up, and laugh, and
hear the slight-est whis-per; I would have faith to keep the

much to dare, I would be brave, for there is much to dare.
love, and lift, I would look up, and laugh, and love, and lift.
path Christ trod, I would have faith to keep the path Christ trod.

290 All the Way My Saviour Leads Me

Fanny J. Crosby

Robert Lowry

1. All the way my Sav-iour leads me; What have I to ask be-side?
2. All the way my Sav-iour leads me, Cheers each wind-ing path I tread,
3. All the way my Sav-iour leads me; Oh, the full-ness of His love!

Can I doubt His ten-der mer-cy, Who through life has been my Guide?
Gives me grace for ev-ery tri-al, Feeds me with the liv-ing bread.
Per-fect rest to me is prom-ised In my Fa-ther's house a-bove.

Heaven-ly peace, di-vin-est com-fort, Here by faith in Him to dwell!
Though my wea-ry steps may fal-ter, And my soul a-thirst may be,
When my spir-it, clothed im-mor-tal, Wings its flight to realms of day,

For I know, what-e'er be-fall me, Je-sus do-eth all things well; well.
Gushing from the Rock be-fore me, Lo! a spring of joy I see; see.
This my song thro' end-less a-ges: Je-sus led me all the way; way.

291 My Saviour First of All

Fanny J. Crosby

Jno. R. Sweney

1. When my life work is end-ed, and I cross the swell-ing tide, When the
2. Oh, the soul-thrill-ing rap-ture when I view His bless-ed face, And the
3. Oh, the dear ones in glo-ry, how they beck-on me to come, And our
4. Thro' the gates to the cit-y in a robe of spot-less white, He will

bright and glorious morning I shall see; I shall know my Re-deem-er when I
lus - tre of His kind-ly beaming eye; How my full heart will praise Him for the
part - ing at the riv - er I re-call; To the sweet vales of E - den they will
lead me where no tears shall ev-er fall; In the glad song of a - ges I shall

reach the oth - er side, And His smile will be the first to wel-come me.
mer - cy, love, and grace, That pre-pares for me a man-sion in the sky.
sing my wel-come home, But I long to meet my Sav-iour first of all.
min - gle with de - light; But I long to meet my Sav-iour first of all.

CHORUS

I shall know Him, I shall know Him, As redeemed by His side I shall stand,
I shall know

I shall know Him, I shall know Him By the print of the nails in His hand.
I shall know

292 Glorious Is Thy Name

B. B. McK.
Majestic

B. B. McKinney

1. Bless-ed Sav-iour, we a-dore Thee, We Thy love and grace pro-claim;
2. Great Re-deem-er, Lord and Mas-ter, Light of all e-ter-nal days;
3. From the throne of heav-en's glo-ry To the cross of sin and shame,
4. Come, O come, im-mor-tal Sav-iour, Come and take Thy roy-al throne;

Thou art might-y, Thou art ho-ly, Glo-rious is Thy match-less name!
Let the saints of ev-ery na-tion Sing Thy just and end-less praise!
Thou didst come to die a ran-som Guilt-y sin-ners to re-claim.
Come and reign, and reign for-ev-er, Be the king-dom all Thine own!

REFRAIN *Faster*

Glo - - - ri-ous, Glo - - - - ri-ous,

Glo-rious is Thy name, O Lord! Glo-rious is Thy name, O Lord!

Glo-rious is Thy name, O Lord! Glo - - - ri-ous,

Glo-rious is Thy name, O Lord!

rit. - - -

Glo - - - ri-ous, Glo-rious is Thy name, O Lord!

Glo-rious is Thy name, O Lord!

293 Lead On, Lead On

B. B. McK.
Unison

B. B. McKinney

1. Lead on, O King of Glo-ry, We will fol-low, fol-low Thee,
2. Lead on, O King of Glo-ry, We will sing the glad re-frain,
3. Lead on, O King of Glo-ry, Lead on for truth and right,

Thy crim-son ban-ner o-ver us Shall a sign of tri-umph be;
Lead on, O Great De-liv-er-er, O-ver all the world's do-main;
Lift high Thy cross e-ter-nal, Lead on, O Prince of Light;

Thou e-ter-nal Christ of Cal-va-ry, Lead us on from sea to sea,
We have heard Thy call to loy-al-ty, We will strive to set men free,
Let re-deem-ing love per-vade the world, Let its ban-ner be un-furled,

Till the day is done, And the crown is won, Lead on, lead on, lead on!
For the cause of right We will stand and fight, Lead us on, O God of Might.
Till the strife shall cease In a calm re-lease, Lead us on, O Prince of Peace.

CHORUS PARTS

On, on, on, on, on; On,

Lead on, lead on, Might-y Man of Gal-i-lee; Lead on, lead
Lead on, lead on, lead on; Lead on,

Lead On, Lead On

on,   on,.......   on;   On,   on,

on,   Thou shalt reign e-ter-nal-ly;   Lead on,   lead on,   To the
lead on, Thou shalt reign   e - ter-nal-ly;   Lead on,   lead on, To the

on,   on,   on,

death we'll fol-low Thee,   Till the day is done And the crown is won, Lead on, lead on!
death   we'll   fol-low Thee,

294   O Happy Day

PHILIP DODDRIDGE   HAPPY DAY   E. F. RIMBAULT

1. { O hap-py day that fixed my choice On Thee, my Sav - iour and my God! }
   { Well may this glow-ing heart re-joice, And tell its rap-tures all a-broad. }
2. { O hap-py bond, that seals my vows To Him who mer - its all my love! }
   { Let cheer-ful an-thems fill His house, While to that sa - cred shrine I move. }
3. { 'Tis done; the great transaction's done! I am my Lord's, and He is mine; }
   { He drew me, and I fol-lowed on, Charmed to confess the voice di-vine. }

REFRAIN   **FINE**

Hap-py day, hap-py day, When Je - sus washed my sins a - way!

D. S.

He taught me how to watch and pray, And live re - joic - ing ev - er - y day;

295 O Holy Night

ADOLF ADAM
Arr. by B. B. McKINNEY

1. O ho - ly night; The stars are bright-ly shin - ing; It is the night of the dear Sav-iour's birth; Long lay the world in sin and er - ror pin - ing, Till He ap-peared, and the soul felt His

2. Led by .... the light Of faith se-rene-ly beam - ing, With glow-ing hearts by His cra - dle to stand; Led by the light of the star so bright-ly gleam - ing, Here came the wise men from O - ri - ent

O Holy Night

ALL PARTS *in Unison Faster*

worth; . . . . .
land; . . . . . A thrill of hope, the wea-ry world re-

joic - es, For yon - der breaks a new and cloud-less morn!

ALL PARTS *in Harmony*

ff

Fall on your knees, O hear the an - gel voic - es, O

night di - vine! . . . . O night . . . when Christ was born! O
O night di-vine! O night was born!

night . . . di - vine! . . . . O night, O night di - vine!
O night

Peace! Be Still!

MARY A. BAKER   H. R. PALMER

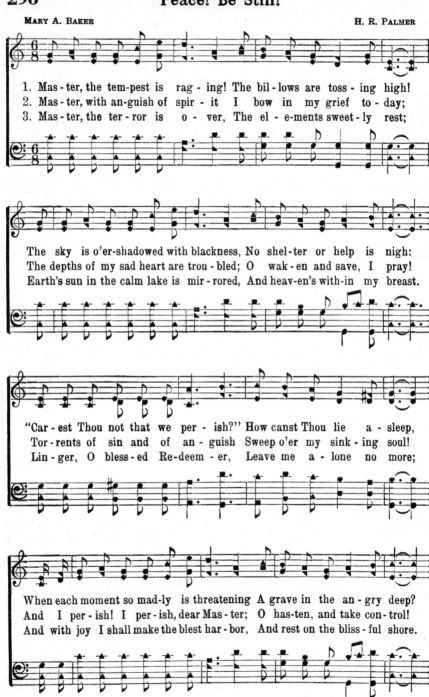

1. Mas-ter, the tem-pest is rag-ing! The bil-lows are toss-ing high!
2. Mas-ter, with an-guish of spir-it I bow in my grief to-day;
3. Mas-ter, the ter-ror is o-ver, The el-e-ments sweet-ly rest;

The sky is o'er-shadowed with blackness, No shel-ter or help is nigh:
The depths of my sad heart are trou-bled; O wak-en and save, I pray!
Earth's sun in the calm lake is mir-rored, And heav-en's with-in my breast.

"Car-est Thou not that we per-ish?" How canst Thou lie a-sleep,
Tor-rents of sin and of an-guish Sweep o'er my sink-ing soul!
Lin-ger, O bless-ed Re-deem-er, Leave me a-lone no more;

When each moment so mad-ly is threatening A grave in the an-gry deep?
And I per-ish! I per-ish, dear Mas-ter; O has-ten, and take con-trol!
And with joy I shall make the blest har-bor, And rest on the bliss-ful shore.

Peace! Be Still!

REFRAIN

"The winds and the waves shall o-bey My will, Peace, be still!"
Peace, be still! peace, be still!

Wheth-er the wrath of the storm-tossed sea, Or de-mons, or men, or what-

cres — — — — — cen — — — — — — do

ev-er it be, No wa-ter can swal-low the ship where lies The Mas-ter of

e-cean and earth and skies; They all shall sweet-ly o-bey My will; Peace, be still!

Peace, be still! They all shall sweet-ly o-bey My will; Peace, peace, be still!

297 Hallelujah for the Cross

HORATIUS BONAR, Arr.   JAMES McGRANAHAN

1. The cross it stand-eth fast, Hal - le - lu - jah, hal-le-lu - jah! De - fy - ing
2. It is the old cross still, Hal - le - lu - jah, hal-le-lu - jah! Its tri-umph
3. 'Twas here the debt was paid, Hal - le - lu - jah, hal-le-lu - jah! Our sins on

ev - ery blast, Hal-le-lu-jah, hal-le - lu-jah! The winds of hell have blown, The
let us tell, Hal-le-lu-jah, hal-le - lu-jah! The grace of God here shone Thro'
Je - sus laid, Hal-le-lu-jah, hal-le - lu-jah! So round the cross we sing Of

cres.

world its hate hath shown, Yet it is not over-thrown, Hal-le-lu-jah for the cross!
Christ the bless-ed Son, Who did for sin a - tone, Hal-le-lu-jah for the cross!
Christ our of - fer - ing, Of Christ our liv-ing King, Hal-le-lu-jah for the cross!

OBBLIGATO DUET SOP. (or TEN.) and ALTO

Hal - le - lu - jah,   hal - le - lu - jah,   Hal - le -

SOPRANO & ALTO*

CHORUS *mp*   Hal - le - lu - jah,   hal - le - lu - jah, Hal - le -

TENOR & BASS

*If desired, the Soprano and Alto may sing the upper staff, omitting the middle staff.

Hallelujah for the Cross!

lu - jah for the cross! Hal - le - lu - jah,

lu - jah for the cross, hal-le-lu-jah for the cross! Hal - le - lu - jah,

hal - le - lu - jah, It shall nev - er suf - fer loss!

hal - le - lu - jah, It shall nev-er suf - fer, nev - er suf - fer loss!

FULL CHORUS

*Hal - le - lu - jah, hal - le - lu - jah, Hal - le - lu - jah for the cross!

cres. *ff*

Hal - le - lu - jah, hal - le - lu - jah, It shall nev - er suf - fer loss!

*For a final ending, all the voices may sing the melody in unison through the last eight measures—
the instrument playing the harmony.

298 He Is Coming, Hallelujah!

B. B. McK.

B. B. McKinney

1. He is com-ing, Hal-le-lu-jah! He is com-ing, Christ the King!
2. He is com-ing, Hal-le-lu-jah! Not a shad-ow, not a tear,

Let the ran-somed of all na-tions Loud ho-san-nas glad-ly sing.
Not a sin, and not a sor-row, When our Sav-iour shall ap-pear.

He is com-ing in His glo-ry, He who died to con-quer sin,
He is com-ing, we are watch-ing With a hope that can-not die;

He who made the full a-tone-ment Shall re-turn to earth a-gain.
O how mar-vel-ous the glo-ry When we see Him by and by.

*Chorus
And He shall reign, ... And He shall reign, ...

For-ev-er, and ev-er, For-ev-er, and ev-er,

*Suggestions from the "Hallelujah Chorus" by Handel.

He Is Coming, Hallelujah!

And He shall reign for - ev - er, and ev - er, and ev - - er,

King of kings, and Lord of lords, King of kings, and Lord of lords!
King of kings, ... King of kings, ...

And He shall reign for - ev - er, and ev - er, and ev - - er,

Hal - le - lu - jah! Hal - le - lu - jah! Hal - le - lu - jah! He shall reign!

He shall reign! .... Hal - le - lu - jah!
Hal-le-lu-jah! Hal-le-lu-jah! Hal-le-lu-jah! Hal-le-lu-jah!

299 God Be with You

ENDEAVOR

J. E. RANKIN

W. G. TOMER

1. God be with you till we meet a-gain, By His coun-sels guide, up-hold you,
2. God be with you till we meet a-gain, 'Neath His wings pro-tect-ing hide you,
3. God be with you till we meet a-gain; When life's per-ils thick confound you,
4. God be with you till we meet a-gain; Keep love's ban-ner float-ing o'er you;

With His sheep se-cure-ly fold you; God be with you till we meet a-gain.
Dai - ly man-na still pro-vide you; God be with you till we meet a-gain.
Put His arms un-fail-ing round you; God be with you till we meet a-gain.
Smite death's threatening wave before you; God be with you till we meet a-gain.

CHORUS

Till we meet, . . . till we meet, Till we meet at Je-sus' feet;

Till we meet, till we meet, Till we meet;

Till we meet, . . . till we meet, God be with you till we meet a-gain.

Till we meet, till we meet,

Thomas Ken   DOXOLOGY   Louis Bourgeois

Praise God, from whom all blessings flow; Praise Him, all crea-tures here be-low;

Praise Him a-bove, ye heaven-ly host; Praise Fa-ther, Son, and Ho-ly Ghost.

301   The Lord Is In His Holy Temple

QUAM DILECTA   George F. Root

The Lord is in His ho-ly tem-ple, The Lord is in His ho-ly

tem-ple; Let all the earth keep si-lence, Let all the earth keep si-lence be-

fore Him, Keep si-lence, keep si-lence be-fore Him. A-MEN.

Glory Be to the Father

GLORIA PATRI
First setting

Anonymous   CHARLES MEINEKE

Glo - ry be to the Fa - ther, and to the Son, and to the Ho - ly Ghost; As it was in the be - gin - ning, is now, and ev - er shall be, world with - out end. A - men, A-men.

Glory Be to the Father

GLORIA PATRI
Second setting

Anonymous   H. W. GREATOREX

Glo - ry be to the Fa - ther, and to the Son, and to the Ho - ly Ghost; As it was in the be - gin - ning, is now, and ev - er shall be, world with - out end. A - men, A - men.

Glory Be to the Father

GLORIA PATRI
Third setting

Old Scottish Chant

Glory be to the *Father*, and to the Son, and to the Ho - ly Ghost;
As it was in the beginning, is *now*, and ev - er shall be, world with - out end. A - men.

305 Tread Softly

FANNY J. CROSBY   W. H. DOANE

Gently   p

1. Be si - lent, be si - lent, A whis - per is heard, Be si - lent, and
2. Be si - lent, be si - lent, For ho - ly this place, This al - tar that
3. Be si - lent, be si - lent, Breathe hum-bly our prayer, A fore-taste of
4. Be si - lent, be si - lent, His mer - cy re - cord, Be si - lent, be

CHORUS

lis - ten, O treas-ure each word!
ech - oes The mes-sage of grace.   Tread soft - ly, tread soft - ly, The
E - den This mo-ment we share.
si - lent And wait on the Lord.   Tread soft-ly here, tread soft-ly here,

p   p   rit.

Mas - ter is here, Tread soft - ly, tread soft - ly, He bids us draw near.
Tread soft-ly here, tread soft-ly here,

306 Bless the Lord, O My Soul

IPPOLITOF-IVANOFF

Bless the Lord, O my soul, Bless-ed art Thou, O Lord. A-MEN.

307 Hear Our Prayer, O Lord

GEORGE WHELPTON

pp Hear our prayer, O Lord, Hear our prayer, O Lord,

In-cline Thine ear to us, And grant us Thy peace. A-MEN.

308 Bless Thou the Gifts

SAMUEL LONGFELLOW   CANONBURY   ROBERT SCHUMANN

Bless Thou the gifts our hands have bro't; Bless Thou the work our hearts have planned;

Ours is the faith, the will, the tho't; The rest, O God, is in Thy hand. A-MEN.

309 All Things Come of Thee, O Lord

Arr. from BEETHOVEN

All things come of Thee, O Lord; and of Thine own have we giv-en Thee. A-MEN.

Amens

RESPONSIVE READINGS

315   PRAISE
Psalm 148

Praise ye the Lord. Praise ye the Lord from the heavens: praise him in the heights.

Praise ye him, all his angels: praise ye him, all his hosts.

Praise ye him, sun and moon; praise him, all ye stars of light.

Praise ye him, ye heavens of heavens and ye waters that be above the heavens.

Let them praise the name of the Lord: for he commanded, and they were created.

He hath also stablished them for ever and ever: he hath made a decree which shall not pass.

Praise the Lord from the earth, ye dragons, and all deeps:

Fire, and hail; snow, and vapours; stormy wind fulfilling his word:

Mountains, and all hills; fruitful trees, and all cedars:

Beasts, and all cattle; creeping things, and flying fowl:

Kings of the earth, and all people; princes, and all judges of the earth.

Both young men, and maidens; old men, and children:

Let them praise the name of the Lord: for his name alone is excellent; his glory is about the earth and heaven.

He also exalteth the horn of his people, the praise of all his saints; even of the children of Israel, a people near unto him. Praise ye the Lord.

316   GOD'S CARE
Psalm 23; John 10:14-18

The Lord is my shepherd; I shall not want.

He maketh me to lie down in green pastures: he leadeth me beside the still waters.

He restoreth my soul: he leadeth me in the paths of righteousness for his name's sake.

Yea, though I walk through the valley of the shadow of death, I will fear no evil: for thou art with me; thy rod and thy staff they comfort me.

Thou preparest a table before me in the presence of mine enemies: thou anointest my head with oil; my cup runneth over.

Surely goodness and mercy shall follow me all the days of my life: and I will dwell in the house of the Lord for ever.

I am the good shepherd and know my sheep, and am known of mine.

As the Father knoweth me, even so know I the Father: and I lay down my life for the sheep.

And other sheep I have, which are not of this fold: them also I must bring, and they shall hear my voice; and there shall be one fold, and one shepherd.

Therefore doth my Father love me, because I lay down my life, that I might take it again.

No man taketh it from me, but I lay it down of myself. I have power to lay it down, and I have power to take it again. This commandment have I received of my Father.

atthew 5:3-12; Psalm 1:1-3; Job
5:17

Blessed are the poor in spirit: for
ieirs is the kingdom of heaven.

**Blessed are they that mourn: for
ьey shall be comforted.**

Blessed are the meek: for they
1all inherit the earth.

**Blessed are they which do hunger
nd thirst after righteousness: for
hey shall be filled.**

Blessed are the merciful: for they
hall obtain mercy.

**Blessed are the pure in heart: for
hey shall see God.**

Blessed are the peacemakers: for
hey shall be called the children of
ϯod.

**Blessed are they which are per-
ecuted for righteousness' sake: for
heirs is the kingdom of heaven.**

Blessed are ye, when men shall re-
ile you, and persecute you, and shall
ay all manner of evil against you
alsely, for my sake.

**Rejoice and be exceeding glad:
or great is your reward in heaven:
or so persecuted they the prophets
vhich were before you.**

Blessed is the man that walketh
1ot in the counsel of the ungodly, nor
standeth in the way of sinners, nor
sitteth in the seat of the scornful.

**But his delight is in the law of the
Lord; and in his law doth he medi-
tate day and night.**

And he shall be like a tree planted
by the rivers of water, that bringeth
forth his fruit in his season; his leaf
also shall not wither; and whatsoever he doeth shall prosper.

**Behold, happy is the man whom
God correcteth: therefore despise not
thou the chastening of the Almighty.**

Psalm 42

As the hart panteth after the
water brooks, so panteth my soul
after thee, O God.

**My soul thirsteth for God, for the
living God; when shall I come and
appear before God?**

My tears have been my meat day
and night, while they continually say
unto me, Where is thy God?

**When I remember these things, I
pour out my soul in me: for I had
gone with the multitude, I went with
them to the house of God, with the
voice of joy and praise, with a multitude that kept holyday.**

Why art thou cast down, O my
soul? and why art thou disquieted in
me? hope thou in God: for I shall yet
praise him for the help of his countenance.

**O my God, my soul is cast down
within me: therefore will I remember thee from the land of Jordan, and
of the Hermonites, from the hill
Mizar.**

Deep calleth unto deep at the noise
of thy waterspouts: all thy waves
and thy billows are gone over me.

**Yet the Lord will command his
lovingkindness in the daytime, and
in the night his song shall be with
me, and my prayer unto the God of
my life.**

I will say unto God my rock, Why
hast thou forgotten me? why go I
mourning because of the oppression
of the enemy?

**As with a sword in my bones, mine
enemies reproach me; while they say
daily unto me, Where is thy God?**

Why art thou cast down, O my
soul? and why art thou disquieted
within me? hope thou in God: for I
shall yet praise him, who is the health
of my countenance, and my God.

319 PERSONAL EVANGELISM
Acts 8:26-37

And the angel of the Lord spake unto Philip, saying, Arise, and go toward the south unto the way that goeth down from Jerusalem unto Gaza which is desert.

And he arose and went: and, behold, a man of Ethiopia, an eunuch of great authority under Candace queen of the Ethiopians who had the charge of all her treasure, and had come to Jerusalem for to worship,

Was returning, and sitting in his chariot read Esaias the prophet.

Then the Spirit said unto Philip, Go near, and join thyself to this chariot.

And Philip ran thither to him, and heard him read the prophet Esaias, and said, Understandest thou what thou readest?

And he said, How can I, except some man should guide me? And he desired Philip that he would come up and sit with him.

The place of the scripture which he read was this, He was led as a sheep to the slaughter; and like a lamb dumb before his shearer, so opened he not his mouth:

In his humiliation his judgment was taken away: and who shall declare his generation? for his life is taken from the earth.

And the eunuch answered Philip, and said, I pray thee, of whom speaketh the prophet this? of himself, or of some other man?

Then Philip opened his mouth, and began at the same scripture, and preached unto him Jesus.

And as they went on their way, they came unto a certain water: and the eunuch said, See, here is water; what doth hinder me to be baptized?

And Philip said, If thou believest with all thine heart, thou mayest

320 SUSTAINING FAITH
Psalm 28; 37:3-4

Unto thee will I cry, O Lord my rock; be not silent to me: lest, if thou be silent to me, I become like them that go down into the pit.

Hear the voice of my supplications, when I cry unto thee, when I lift up my hands toward the holy oracle.

Draw me not away with the wicked, and with the workers of iniquity which speak peace to their neighbours, but mischief is in their hearts.

Give them according to their deeds and according to the wickedness of their endeavours: give them after the work of their hands; render to them their desert.

Because they regard not the works of the Lord nor the operation of his hands he shall destroy them and not build them up.

Blessed be the Lord, because he hath heard the voice of my supplications.

The Lord is my strength and my shield; my heart trusted in him, and I am helped: therefore my heart greatly rejoiceth; and with my song will I praise him.

The Lord is their strength, and he is the saving strength of his anointed.

Save thy people, and bless thine inheritance: feed them also, and lift them up for ever.

Trust in the Lord, and do good; so shalt thou dwell in the land, and verily thou shalt be fed.

Delight thyself also in the Lord, and he shall give thee the desires of thine heart.

321 THE LORD'S MERCIES

Lamentations 3:18-33
Psalm 100:2, 4-5

And I said, My strength and my hope is perished from the Lord:

Remembering mine affliction and my misery, the wormwood and the gall.

My soul hath them still in remembrance, and is humbled in me.

This I recall to my mind therefore have I hope.

It is of the Lord's mercies that we are not consumed, because his compassions fail not.

They are new every morning: great is thy faithfulness.

The Lord is my portion, saith my soul; therefore will I hope in him.

The Lord is good unto them that wait for him, to the soul that seeketh him.

It is good that a man should both hope and quietly wait for the salvation of the Lord.

It is good for a man that he bear the yoke in his youth.

He sitteth alone and keepeth silence, because he hath borne it upon him.

He putteth his mouth in the dust; if so be there may be hope.

He giveth his cheek to him that smiteth him: he is filled full with reproach.

For the Lord will not cast off for ever:

But though he cause grief, yet will he have compassion according to the multitude of his mercies.

For he doth not afflict willingly nor grieve the children of men.

Serve the Lord with gladness: come before his presence with singing.

Enter into his gates with thanksgiving, and into his courts with praise: be thankful unto him, and bless his name.

For the Lord is good; his mercy is everlasting; and his truth endureth to all generations.

322 THE PLEA FOR MERCY

Psalm 51:1-12

Have mercy on me, O God, according to thy lovingkindness: according unto the multitude of thy tender mercies blot out my transgressions.

Wash me throughly from mine iniquity, and cleanse me from my sin.

For I acknowledge my transgressions: and my sin is ever before me.

Against thee, thee only, have I sinned, and done this evil in thy sight: that thou mightest be justified when thou speakest, and be clear when thou judgest.

Behold, I was shapen in iniquity; and in sin did my mother conceive me.

Behold, thou desirest truth in the inward parts: and in the hidden part thou shalt make me to know wisdom.

Purge me with hyssop, and I shall be clean: wash me, and I shall be whiter than snow.

Make me to hear joy and gladness; that the bones which thou hast broken may rejoice.

Hide thy face from my sins, and blot out all mine iniquities.

Create in me a clean heart, O God; and renew a right spirit within me.

Cast me not away from thy presence; and take not thy holy spirit from me.

Restore unto me the joy of thy salvation; and uphold me with thy free spirit.

323 GRACIOUS EXHORTATION
Psalm 103:1-13, 19, 21-22

Bless the Lord, O my soul: and all that is within me, bless his holy name.

Bless the Lord, O my soul, and forget not all his benefits:

Who forgiveth all thine iniquities; who healeth all thy diseases;

Who redeemeth thy life from destruction, who crowneth thee with lovingkindness and tender mercies;

Who satisfieth thy mouth with good things; so that thy youth is renewed like the eagle's.

The Lord executeth righteousness and judgment for all that are oppressed.

He made known his ways unto Moses, his acts unto the children of Israel.

The Lord is merciful and gracious, slow to anger, and plenteous in mercy.

He will not always chide: neither will he keep his anger for ever.

He hath not dealt with us after our sins; nor rewarded us according to our iniquities.

For as the heaven is high above the earth, so great is his mercy toward them that fear him.

As far as the east is from the west, so far hath he removed our transgressions from us.

Like as a father pitieth his children, so the Lord pitieth them that fear him.

The Lord hath prepared his throne in the heavens; and his kingdom ruleth over all.

Bless ye the Lord, all ye his hosts; ye ministers of his, that do his pleasure.

Bless the Lord, all his works in all places of his dominion: bless the Lord, O my soul.

324 TIMELY EXHORTATIONS

Ephesians 6:1-4, 10-11, 13-18

Children, obey your parents in the Lord: for this is right.

Honour thy father and mother which is the first commandment with promise;

That it may be well with thee and thou mayest live long on the earth.

And, ye fathers, provoke not your children to wrath: but bring them up in the nurture and admonition of the Lord.

Finally, my brethren, be strong in the Lord, and in the power of his might.

Put on the whole armour of God, that ye may be able to stand against the wiles of the devil.

Wherefore take unto you the whole armour of God, that ye may be able to withstand in the evil day, and having done all, to stand.

Stand therefore, having your loins girt about with truth, having on the breastplate of righteousness.

And your feet shod with the preparation of the gospel of peace;

Above all, taking the shield of faith, wherewith ye shall be able to quench all the fiery darts of the wicked.

And take the helmet of salvation, and the sword of the Spirit, which is the word of God:

Praying always with all prayer and supplication in the Spirit and watching thereunto with all perseverance and supplication for all saints.

325   FALSE TRUST
Mark 10:17-27

And when he was gone forth into he way, there came one running, nd kneeled to him, and asked him, ood Master, what shall I do that may inherit eternal life?

And Jesus said unto him, Why allest thou me good? there is none ood but one, that is, God.

Thou knowest the commandments,)o not commit adultery, Do not kill,)o not steal, Do not bear false wit-ess, Defraud not, Honour thy fa-her and mother.

And he answered and said unto im, Master, all these have I ob-erved from my youth.

Then Jesus beholding him loved im, and said unto him, One thing hou lackest: go thy way, sell what-oever thou hast, and give to the oor, and thou shalt have treasure n heaven: and come, take up the ross, and follow me.

And he was sad at that saying, and vent away grieved: for he had reat possessions.

And Jesus looked round about, nd saith unto his disciples, How ardly shall they that have riches nter into the kingdom of God!

And the disciples were astonished t his words. But Jesus answered gain, and saith unto them, Children, ow hard is it for them that trust in iches to enter into the kingdom of iod!

It is easier for a camel to go hrough the eye of a needle, than or a rich man to enter into the ingdom of God.

And they were astonished out of neasure, saying among themselves, Vho then can be saved?

And Jesus looking upon them aith, With men it is impossible, but not with God: for with God all things are possible.

326   SECURITY
Psalm 91:1-12, 14

He that dwelleth in the secret place of the most High shall abide under the shadow of the Almighty.

I will say of the Lord, He is my refuge and my fortress: my God; in him will I trust.

Surely he shall deliver thee from the snare of the fowler, and from the noisome pestilence.

He shall cover thee with his feathers, and under his wings shalt thou trust: his truth shall be thy shield and buckler.

Thou shalt not be afraid for the terror by night; nor for the arrow that flieth by day;

Nor for the pestilence that walketh in darkness; nor for the destruction that wasteth at noonday.

A thousand shall fall at thy side, and ten thousand at thy right hand; but it shall not come nigh thee.

Only with thine eyes shalt thou behold and see the reward of the wicked.

Because thou hast made the Lord, which is my refuge, even the most High, thy habitation;

There shall no evil befall thee, neither shall any plague come nigh thy dwelling.

For he shall give his angels charge over thee, to keep thee in all thy ways.

They shall bear thee up in their hands, lest thou dash thy foot against a stone.

Because he hath set his love upon me, therefore will I deliver him: I will set him on high, because he hath known my name.

327 CHRISTIAN CONFIDENCE
Psalm 46; 47:6-8

God is our refuge and strength, a very present help in trouble. Therefore will not we fear, though the earth be removed, and though the mountains be carried into the midst of the sea;

Though the waters thereof roar and be troubled, though the mountains shake with the swelling thereof. Selah.

There is a river, the streams whereof shall make glad the city of God, the holy place of the tabernacles of the most High.

God is in the midst of her; she shall not be moved: God shall help her, and that right early.

The heathen raged, the kingdoms were moved: he uttered his voice, the earth melted.

The Lord of hosts is with us; the God of Jacob is our refuge. Selah.

Come, behold the works of the Lord, what desolations he hath made in the earth.

He maketh wars to cease unto the end of the earth; he breaketh the bow, and cutteth the spear in sunder; he burneth the chariot in the fire.

Be still, and know that I am God: I will be exalted among the heathen, I will be exalted in the earth.

The Lord of hosts is with us; the God of Jacob is our refuge. Selah.

Sing praises to God, sing praises: sing praises unto our King, sing praises.

For God is the King of all the earth: sing ye praises with understanding.

God reigneth over the heathen: God sitteth upon the throne of his holiness.

328 NO CONDEMNATION
Romans 8:1-11

There is therefore now no condemnation to them which are in Christ Jesus, who walk not after the flesh, but after the Spirit.

For the law of the Spirit of life in Christ Jesus hath made me free from the law of sin and death.

For what the law could not do, in that it was weak through the flesh, God sending his own Son in the likeness of sinful flesh, and for sin, condemned sin in the flesh:

That the righteousness of the law might be fulfilled in us, who walk not after the flesh, but after the Spirit.

For they that are after the flesh do mind the things of the flesh; but they that are after the Spirit the things of the Spirit.

For to be carnally minded is death; but to be spiritually minded is life and peace.

Because the carnal mind is enmity against God: for it is not subject to the law of God, neither indeed can be.

So then they that are in the flesh cannot please God.

But ye are not in the flesh, but in the Spirit, if so be that the Spirit of God dwell in you. Now if any man have not the Spirit of Christ, he is none of his.

And if Christ be in you, the body is dead because of sin; but the Spirit is life because of righteousness.

But if the Spirit of him that raised up Jesus from the dead dwell in you, he that raised up Christ from the dead shall also quicken your mortal bodies by his Spirit that dwelleth in you.

329 WISE INVESTMENT
Matthew 6:19-26, 28-30

Lay not up for yourselves treasures upon earth, where moth and rust doth corrupt, and where thieves break through and steal:

But lay up for yourselves treasures in heaven, where neither moth nor rust doth corrupt, and where thieves do not break through nor steal:

For where your treasure is, there will your heart be also.

The light of the body is the eye: if therefore thine eye be single, thy whole body shall be full of light.

But if thine eye be evil, thy whole body shall be full of darkness. If therefore the light that is in thee be darkness, how great is that darkness!

No man can serve two masters: for either he will hate the one, and love the other; or else he will hold to the one, and despise the other. Ye cannot serve God and mammon.

Therefore I say unto you, Take no thought for your life, what ye shall eat, or what ye shall drink; nor yet for your body, what ye shall put on. Is not the life more than meat, and the body than raiment?

Behold the fowls of the air: for they sow not, neither do they reap, nor gather into barns; yet your heavenly Father feedeth them. Are ye not much better than they?

And why take ye thought for raiment? Consider the lilies of the field, how they grow; they toil not, neither do they spin:

And yet I say unto you, That even Solomon in all his glory was not arrayed like one of these.

Wherefore, if God so clothe the grass of the field, which to day is, and to morrow is cast into the oven, shall he not much more clothe you, O ye of little faith?

330 THE PROFIT SYSTEM
Luke 19:12-13, 15-23

He said therefore, A certain nobleman went into a far country to receive for himself a kingdom, and to return.

And he called his ten servants, and delivered them ten pounds, and said unto them, Occupy till I come.

And it came to pass, that when he was returned, having received the kingdom, then he commanded these servants to be called unto him, to whom he had given the money, that he might know how much every man had gained by trading.

Then came the first, saying, Lord, thy pound hath gained ten pounds.

And he said unto him, Well, thou good servant: because thou hast been faithful in a very little, have thou authority over ten cities.

And the second came, saying, Lord, thy pound hath gained five pounds.

And he said likewise to him, Be thou also over five cities.

And another came, saying, Lord, behold, here is thy pound which I have kept laid up in a napkin:

For I feared thee, because thou art an austere man: thou takest up that thou layest not down, and reapest that thou didst not sow.

And he saith unto him, Out of thine own mouth will I judge thee, thou wicked servant. Thou knewest that I was an austere man, taking up that I laid not down, and reaping that I did not sow:

Wherefore then gavest not thou my money into the bank, that at my coming I might have required mine own with usury?

331 COMMUNION WITH GOD
Psalm 84; 86:11-12

How amiable are thy tabernacles, O Lord of hosts!

My soul longeth, yea, even fainteth for the courts of the Lord: my heart and my flesh crieth out for the living God.

Yea, the sparrow hath found an house, and the swallow a nest for herself, where she may lay her young, even thine altars, O Lord of hosts, my King, and my God.

Blessed are they that dwell in thy house: they will be still praising thee. Selah.

Blessed is the man whose strength is in thee; in whose heart are the ways of them.

Who passing through the valley of Baca make it a well; the rain also filleth the pools.

They go from strength to strength, every one of them in Zion appeareth before God.

O Lord God of hosts, hear my prayer: give ear, O God of Jacob. Selah.

Behold, O God our shield, and look upon the face of thine anointed.

For a day in thy courts is better than a thousand. I had rather be a doorkeeper in the house of my God, than to dwell in the tents of wickedness.

For the Lord God is the sun and shield: the Lord will give grace and glory; no good thing will he withhold from them that walk uprightly.

O Lord of hosts, blessed is the man that trusteth in thee.

Teach me thy way, O Lord; I will walk in thy truth: unite my heart to fear thy name.

I will praise thee, O Lord my God, with all my heart: and I will glorify thy name for evermore.

332 MUTUAL LOVE
John 15:9-19

As the Father hath loved me, so have I loved you: continue ye in my love.

If ye keep my commandments, ye shall abide in my love; even as I have kept my Father's commandments, and abide in his love.

These things have I spoken unto you that my joy might remain in you, and that your joy might be full.

This is my commandment, That ye love one another, as I have loved you.

Greater love hath no man than this, that a man lay down his life for his friends.

Ye are my friends, if ye do whatsoever I command you.

Henceforth I call you not servants; for the servant knoweth not what his lord doeth: but I have called you friends; for all things that I have heard of my Father I have made known unto you.

Ye have not chosen me, but I have chosen you, and ordained you, that ye should go and bring forth fruit, and that your fruit should remain: that whatsoever ye shall ask of the Father in my name, he may give it you.

These things I command you, that ye love one another.

If the world hate you, ye know that it hated me before it hated you.

If ye were of the world, the world would love his own: but because ye are not of the world, but I have chosen you out of the world, therefore the world hateth you.

333 GOD'S MAJESTY
Psalm 97:1-2, 4-12; 98:1-3

The Lord reigneth; let the earth rejoice; let the multitude of isles be glad thereof.

Clouds and darkness are round about him: righteousness and judgment are the habitation of his throne.

His lightnings enlightened the world: the earth saw, and trembled.

The hills melted like wax at the presence of the Lord, at the presence of the Lord of the whole earth.

The heavens declare his righteousness, and all the people see his glory.

Confounded be all they that serve graven images, that boast themselves of idols: worship him, all ye gods.

Zion heard, and was glad: and the daughters of Judah rejoiced because of thy judgments, O Lord.

For thou, Lord, art high above all the earth: thou art exalted far above all gods.

Ye that love the Lord, hate evil: he preserveth the souls of his saints; he delivereth them out of the hand of the wicked.

Light is sown for the righteous, and gladness for the upright in heart.

Rejoice in the Lord, ye righteous; and give thanks at the remembrance of his holiness.

O sing unto the Lord a new song; for he hath done marvellous things: his right hand, and his holy arm, hath gotten him the victory.

The Lord hath made known his salvation: his righteousness hath he openly shewed in the sight of the heathen.

He hath remembered his mercy and his truth toward the house of Israel: all the ends of the earth have seen the salvation of our God.

334 ON MARS' HILL
Acts 17:22-31

Then Paul stood in the midst of Mars' hill, and said, Ye men of Athens, I perceive that in all things ye are too superstitious.

For as I passed by, and beheld your devotions, I found an altar with this inscription, TO THE UN-KNOWN GOD. Whom therefore ye ignorantly worship, him declare I unto you.

God that made the world and all things therein, seeing that he is Lord of heaven and earth, dwelleth not in temples made with hands;

Neither is worshipped with men's hands as though he needed any thing, seeing he giveth to all life, and breath, and all things;

And hath made of one blood all nations of men for to dwell on all the face of the earth, and hath determined the times before appointed, and the bounds of their habitation;

That they should seek the Lord, if haply they might feel after him, and find him, though he be not far from every one of us:

For in him we live, and move, and have our being; as certain also of your own poets have said, For we are also his offspring.

Forasmuch then as we are the offspring of God, we ought not to think that the Godhead is like unto gold, or silver, or stone, graven by art and man's device.

And the times of this ignorance God winked at; but now commandeth all men every where to repent:

Because he hath appointed a day, in which he will judge the world in righteousness by that man whom he hath ordained; whereof he hath given assurance unto all men, in that he hath raised him from the dead.

335 WORDS OF WISDOM
Proverbs 22:1-12, 15-17

A good name is rather to be chosen than great riches, and loving favour rather than silver and gold.

The rich and poor meet together: the Lord is the maker of them all.

A prudent man foreseeth the evil, and hideth himself: but the simple pass on, and are punished.

By humility and the fear of the Lord are riches, and honour, and life.

Thorns and snares are in the way of the froward: he that doth keep his soul shall be far from them.

Train up a child in the way he should go: when he is old, he will not depart from it.

The rich ruleth over the poor, and the borrower is servant to the lender.

He that soweth iniquity shall reap vanity: and the rod of his anger shall fail.

He that hath a bountiful eye shall be blessed; for he giveth of his bread to the poor.

Cast out the scorner, and contention shall go out; yea, strife and reproach shall cease.

He that loveth pureness of heart, for the grace of his lips the king shall be his friend.

The eyes of the Lord preserve knowledge, and he overthroweth the words of the transgressor.

Foolishness is bound in the heart of a child; but the rod of correction shall drive it far from him.

He that oppresseth the poor to increase his riches, and he that giveth to the rich, shall surely come to want.

Bow down thine ear, and hear the words of the wise, and apply thine heart unto my knowledge.

336 COUNSEL TO YOUTH
Ecclesiastes 11:9-10; 12:1-7

Rejoice, O young man, in thy youth; and let thy heart cheer thee in the days of thy youth, and walk in the ways of thine heart, and in the sight of thine eyes: but know thou, that for all these things God will bring thee into judgment.

Therefore remove sorrow from thy heart, and put away evil from thy flesh: for childhood and youth are vanity.

Remember now thy Creator in the days of thy youth, while the evil days come not, nor the years draw nigh, when thou shalt say, I have no pleasure in them;

While the sun, or the light, or the moon, or the stars, be not darkened, nor the clouds return after the rain:

In the days when the keepers of the house shall tremble, and the strong men shall bow themselves, and the grinders cease because they are few, and those that look out of the windows be darkened,

And the doors shall be shut in the streets, when the sound of the grinding is low, and he shall rise up at the voice of the bird, and all the daughters of musick shall be brought low;

Also when they shall be afraid of that which is high, and fears shall be in the way, and the almond tree shall flourish, and the grasshopper shall be a burden, and desire shall fail: because man goeth to his long home, and the mourners go about the streets:

Or ever the silver cord be loosed, or the golden bowl be broken, or the pitcher be broken at the fountain, or the wheel broken at the cistern.

Then shall the dust return to the earth as it was: and the spirit shall return unto God who gave it.

337 THE SUFFERING CHRIST
Isaiah 53:1-10

Who hath believed our report? and to whom is the arm of the Lord revealed?

For he shall grow up before him as a tender plant, and as a root out of a dry ground: he hath no form nor comeliness; and when we shall see him, there is no beauty that we should desire him.

He is despised and rejected of men: a man of sorrows, and acquainted with grief: and we hid as it were our faces from him; he was despised, and we esteemed him not.

Surely he hath borne our griefs, and carried our sorrows: yet we did esteem him stricken, smitten of God and afflicted.

But he was wounded for our transgressions, he was bruised for our iniquities: the chastisement of our peace was upon him; and with his stripes we are healed.

All we like sheep have gone astray; we have turned every one to his own way; and the Lord hath laid on him the iniquity of us all.

He was oppressed, and he was afflicted, yet he opened not his mouth: he is brought as a lamb to the slaughter, and as a sheep before her shearers is dumb, so he openeth not his mouth.

He was taken from prison and from judgment: and who shall declare his generation? for he was cut off out of the land of the living: for the transgression of my people was he stricken.

And he made his grave with the wicked, and with the rich in his death; because he had done no violence, neither was any deceit in his mouth.

Yet it pleased the Lord to bruise him; he hath put him to grief.

338 FRUIT OF THE SPIRIT
Galatians 5:22-26; 6:1-9

But the fruit of the Spirit is love, joy, peace, longsuffering, gentleness, goodness, faith,

Meekness, temperance: against such there is no law.

And they that are Christ's have crucified the flesh with the affections and lusts.

If we live in the Spirit, let us also walk in the Spirit.

Let us not be desirous of vain glory, provoking one another, envying one another.

Brethren, if a man be overtaken in a fault, ye which are spiritual, restore such an one in the spirit of meekness; considering thyself, lest thou also be tempted.

Bear ye one another's burdens, and so fulfil the law of Christ.

For if a man think himself to be something, when he is nothing, he deceiveth himself.

But let every man prove his own work, and then shall he have rejoicing in himself alone, and not in another.

For every man shall bear his own burden.

Let him that is taught in the word communicate unto him that teacheth in all good things.

Be not deceived; God is not mocked: for whatsoever a man soweth, that shall he also reap.

For he that soweth to his flesh shall of the flesh reap corruption; but he that soweth to the Spirit shall of the Spirit reap life everlasting.

And let us not be weary in well doing: for in due season we shall reap, if we faint not.

Luke 15:11-22

And he said, A certain man had two sons:

And the younger of them said to his father, Father, give me the portion of goods that falleth to me. And he divided unto them his living.

And not many days after the younger son gathered all together, and took his journey into a far country, and there wasted his substance with riotous living.

And when he had spent all, there arose a mighty famine in that land; and he began to be in want.

And he went and joined himself to a citizen of that country; and he sent him into his fields to feed swine.

And he would fain have filled his belly with the husks that the swine did eat: and no man gave unto him.

And when he came to himself, he said, How many hired servants of my father's have bread enough and to spare, and I perish with hunger!

I will arise and go to my father, and will say unto him, Father, I have sinned against heaven, and before thee,

And am no more worthy to be called thy son: make me as one of thy hired servants.

And he arose, and came to his father. But when he was yet a great way off, his father saw him, and had compassion, and ran, and fell on his neck, and kissed him.

And the son said unto him, Father, I have sinned against heaven, and in thy sight, and am no more worthy to be called thy son.

But the father said to his servants, Bring forth the best robe, and put it on him; and put a ring on his hand, and shoes on his feet.

John 11:20-28, 30-32

Then Martha, as soon as she heard that Jesus was coming, went and met him: but Mary sat still in the house.

Then said Martha unto Jesus, Lord, if thou hadst been here, my brother had not died.

But I know, that even now, whatsoever thou wilt ask of God, God will give it thee.

Jesus saith unto her, Thy brother shall rise again.

Martha saith unto him, I know that he shall rise again in the resurrection at the last day.

Jesus said unto her, I am the resurrection, and the life: he that believeth in me, though he were dead, yet shall he live:

And whosoever liveth and believeth in me shall never die. Believeth thou this?

She saith unto him, Yea, Lord: I believe that thou art the Christ, the Son of God, which should come into the world.

And when she had so said, she went her way, and called Mary her sister secretly, saying, The Master is come, and calleth for thee.

Now Jesus was not yet come into the town, but was in that place where Martha met him.

The Jews then which were with her in the house, and comforted her, when they saw Mary that she rose up hastily and went out, followed her, saying, She goeth unto the grave to weep there.

Then when Mary was come where Jesus was, and saw him, she fell down at his feet, saying unto him, Lord, if thou hadst been here, my brother had not died.

341 THE LOVE POEM
1 Corinthians 13

Though I speak with the tongues of men and of angels, and have not love, I am become as sounding brass, or a tinkling cymbal.

And though I have the gift of prophecy, and understand all mysteries, and all knowledge; and though I have all faith, so that I could remove mountains, and have not love, I am nothing.

And though I bestow all my goods to feed the poor, and though I give my body to be burned, and have not love, it profiteth me nothing.

Love suffereth long, and is kind; love envieth not; love vaunteth not itself, is not puffed up,

Doth not behave itself unseemly, seeketh not her own, is not easily provoked, thinketh no evil;

Rejoiceth not in iniquity, but rejoiceth in the truth;

Beareth all things, believeth all things, hopeth all things, endureth all things.

Love never faileth: but whether there be prophecies, they shall fail; whether there be tongues, they shall cease; whether there be knowledge, it shall vanish away.

For we know in part, and we prophesy in part.

But when that which is perfect is come, then that which is in part shall be done away.

When I was a child, I spake as a child, I understood as a child, I thought as a child: but when I became a man, I put away childish things.

For now we see through a glass, darkly; but then face to face: now I know in part; but then shall I know even as also I am known.

And now abideth faith, hope, love, these three; but the greatest of these is love.

342 ON CALVARY
Luke 23:34-43

And when they were come to the place, which is called Calvary, there they crucified him, and the malefactors, one on the right hand, and the other on the left.

Then said Jesus, Father, forgive them; for they know not what they do. And they parted his raiment, and cast lots.

And the people stood beholding. And the rulers also with them derided him, saying, He saved others; let him save himself, if he be Christ, the chosen of God.

And the soldiers also mocked him, coming to him, and offering him vinegar,

And saying, If thou be the king of the Jews, save thyself.

And a superscription also was written over him in letters of Greek, and Latin, and Hebrew, THIS IS KING OF THE JEWS.

And one of the malefactors which were hanged railed on him, saying, If thou be Christ, save thyself and us.

But the other answering rebuked him, saying, Dost not thou fear God, seeing thou art in the same condemnation?

And we indeed justly; for we receive the due reward of our deeds: but this man hath done nothing amiss.

And he said unto Jesus, Lord, remember me when thou comest into thy kingdom.

And Jesus said unto him, Verily I say unto thee, To day shalt thou be with me in paradise.

343 HEAVENLY RECOGNITION
Luke 16:19-29

There was a certain rich man, which was clothed in purple and fine linen, and fared sumptuously every day:

And there was a certain beggar named Lazarus, which was laid at his gate full of sores,

And desiring to be fed with the crumbs which fell from the rich man's table: moreover the dogs came and licked his sores.

And it came to pass, that the beggar died, and was carried by the angels into Abraham's bosom: the rich man also died, and was buried;

And in hell he lift up his eyes, being in torments, and seeth Abraham afar off, and Lazarus in his bosom.

And he cried and said, Father Abraham, have mercy on me, and send Lazarus, that he may dip the tip of his finger in water, and cool my tongue; for I am tormented in this flame.

But Abraham said, Son, remember that thou in thy lifetime receivest thy good things, and likewise Lazarus evil things: but now he is comforted, and thou art tormented.

And beside all this, between us and you there is a great gulf fixed: so that they which would pass from hence to you cannot; neither can they pass to us, that would come from thence.

Then he said, I pray thee therefore, father, that thou wouldest send him to my father's house;

For I have five brethren; that he may testify unto them, lest they also come into this place of torment.

Abraham saith unto him, They have Moses and the prophets; let them hear them.

344 THE CHRISTIAN'S HOME
John 14:1-3; Revelation 21:1-7

Let not your heart be troubled: ye believe in God, believe also in me.

In my Father's house are many mansions: if it were not so, I would have told you. I go to prepare a place for you.

And if I go and prepare a place for you, I will come again, and receive you unto myself; that where I am, there ye may be also.

And I saw a new heaven and a new earth: for the first heaven and the first earth were passed away; and there was no more sea.

And I John saw the holy city, new Jerusalem, coming down from God out of heaven, prepared as a bride adorned for her husband.

And I heard a great voice out of heaven saying, Behold, the tabernacle of God is with men, and he will dwell with them, and they shall be his people, and God himself shall be with them, and be their God.

And God shall wipe away all tears from their eyes; and there shall be no more death, neither sorrow, nor crying, neither shall there be any more pain: for the former things are passed away.

And he that sat upon the throne said, Behold, I make all things new. And he said unto me, Write: for these words are true and faithful.

And he said unto me, It is done. I am Alpha and Omega, the beginning and the end. I will give unto him that is athirst of the fountain of the water of life freely.

He that overcometh shall inherit all things; and I will be his God, and he shall be my son.

TOPICAL INDEX

Adoration

A Mighty Fortress................ 76
All Hail the Power...........120-121
Crown Him With................ 1
Fairest Lord Jesus................ 215
Glorious Is Thy Name......... 292
Majestic Sweetness 170
O Come, All Ye Faithful..... 143
The Great Physician........... 267

Affliction

Have Faith in God............... 52
I Must Tell Jesus................. 36
Jesus, Saviour, Pilot........... 176
O Love that Wilt Not Let... 219
Take the Name of Jesus..... 233
What a Friend.................... 160

Aspiration

All On the Altar................. 102
Breathe On Me................... 275
Close to Thee.................... 175
Higher Ground................. 131
I Would Be Like Thee........ 282
More About Jesus 169
O Master, Let Me Walk...... 202
Saviour, More than Life...... 235

Assurance

A Mighty Fortress 76
Blessed Assurance 3
He Hideth My Soul............ 30
He Leadeth Me 165
It Is Well with My............. 33
My Hope Is Built............... 22
O God, Our Help............... 193
O Happy Day 294
Rock of Ages 264
Safe in the Arms............... 88
Saved, Saved 44
Standing on the Promises...... 17
The Haven of Rest............. 272

Atonement

Alas! and Did My Saviour.... 211
At the Cross..................... 112
Beneath the Cross............. 262
Blessed Redeemer 41
I Gave My Life for Thee..... 185
Jesus Paid It All................ 194
My Hope Is Built............... 22
Nothing But the Blood........ 188
Once for All 84
Out of the Golden Palaces.... 259
Rock of Ages 264
There Is a Fountain........... 75
There Is a Green Hill........ 98
When I Survey.................. 191

Baptism

Christ Arose 139
Follow On 132
I've Found a Friend............ 70
Jesus, I My Cross............... 72
My Faith Looks Up............. 198
O Happy Day 294
Take My Life and.............. 172
Trust and Obey................. 104
Where He Leads Me............ 166

Bible

Break Thou the Bread......... 237
Holy Bible Book Divine....... 216
How Firm a Foundation....... 171
My Mother's Bible............. 285
More About Jesus.............. 169
Thy Word Have I Hid......... 107
Wonderful Words of Life...... 221

Blood

Alas! and Did.................... 212
Jesus Paid It All................ 194
Not All the Blood of Beasts.. 208

Nothing But the Blood........ 188
There Is a Fountain............ 75
When I Survey................... 191

Brotherhood

Am I a Soldier................... 199
Blest Be the Tie................ 218
Jesus Calls Us................... 159
Lead On, O King............... 200
Let the Lower Lights.......... 265
Onward, Christian Soldiers.. 9
Stand Up for Jesus............. 8

Children

Child's Morning Hymn.......... 240
Good Morning to You.......... 244
I Was Glad When They....... 245
Jesus Loves Even Me........... 273
Jesus Loves Me.................. 243
Jesus Loves the Little......... 241
John Three Sixteen............. 232
Praise Him, All Ye............. 242
The Happy Story Hour......... 246
Beautiful Redeemer 13

Choir Selections

Blessed Redeemer 41
Breathe On Me.................. 275
Christ the Lord Is Risen..... 64
Glorious Is Thy Name......... 292
Hallelujah for the Cross...... 297
He Is Coming, Hallelujah!.... 298
He Lives 48
In Thy Holy Temple........... 288
Lead On, Lead On.............. 293
Near to the Heart of God.... 225
'Neath the Old Olive Trees.. 40
O Holy Night.................... 295
Peace! Be Still!................. 296
Rejoice 49
Wonderful, Wonderful Jesus. 35

Christmas

Hark, Hark My Soul............ 32
Hark! the Herald Angels..... 142
I Heard the Bells............... 148
It Came Upon the Midnight.. 141
O Come, All Ye Faithful...... 143
O Holy Night.................... 295
O Little Town................... 144
Silent Night..................... 146
While Shepherds Watched..... 147

Christ's Return

He Is Coming, Hallelujah!.... 298
He Lives on High............... 83
One Day 28
Praise Him! Praise Him!..... 2
Ready 164
There's a Great Day.......... 209
Will Jesus Find Us............. 37

Choruses (Short)

Fall Fresh on Me............... 229
I Was Glad 245
Jesus Loves the Little......... 241
John Three Sixteen............. 232
Lead Me to Some Soul........ 239
Lord, Lay Some Soul.......... 238
The Rainbow 257
Whisper a Prayer............... 266

Church

A Mighty Fortress 76
Blest Be the Tie................ 218
Faith of Our Fathers.......... 201
I Love Thy Kingdom............ 196
Onward, Christian Soldiers... 9
The Church's One Founda-
   tion 66
The Kingdom is Coming........ 91
The Son of God Goes........... 65
Zion Stands with Hills........ 287

Closing Hymns

Abide with Me................... 179
Day Is Dying.................... 130
God Be With You................ 299
Saviour, Like a Shepherd.... 57
Softly Now the Light.......... 263
Sun of My Soul................. 177
Take the Name of Jesus....... 233

Comfort

All the Way My Saviour...... 290
He Leadeth Me 165
How Firm a Foundation....... 171
I Must Tell Jesus.............. 36
I've Found a Friend............ 70
Lead Kindly Light.............. 217
Rock of Ages 264
What a Friend................... 160
When the Morning Comes.... 134

Confession

Beautiful Redeemer 13
Have Thine Own Way.......... 253
I Am Resolved.................. 20
I Need Thee Every Hour...... 173
I Surrender All................. 103
Just As I Am................... 162
Where He Leads Me............ 166

Conflict

A Mighty Fortress 76
Am I a Soldier.................. 199
Faith of Our Fathers.......... 201
Jesus Shall Reign.............. 150
Lead On, O King............... 200
My Soul Be on Thy Guard... 174
Onward, Christian Soldiers... 9
Where He Leads Me............ 166
Stand Up for Jesus............. 8

Consecration

Beautiful Redeemer 13
Breathe On Me 275
Close to Thee................... 175
Follow On 132
Give of Your Best.............. 286
Have Thine Own Way........... 253
I Am Thine, O Lord........... 6
I Gave My Life for Thee..... 185
I Would Be Like Thee......... 282
I Would Be True................ 289
Jesus Calls Us................... 159
Jesus, I My Cross............... 72
Living for Jesus................ 96
Make Me a Channel............. 27
More Love to Thee............. 227
My Jesus, I Love Thee........ 261
O Jesus, I Have Promised..... 195
O Master, Let Me Walk....... 202
Our Best 87
Ready 164
Something for Thee............ 149
Take My Life.................... 172
When I Survey................... 191
Wherever He Leads............. 99

Cross

Am I a Soldier.................. 199
At the Cross.................... 112
Beneath the Cross............. 262
Glory to His Name............. 155
In the Cross of Christ........ 180
Jesus, I My Cross............... 72
Must Jesus Bear................ 154
Near the Cross.................. 156
The Old Rugged Cross......... 34
There Is a Green Hill......... 98
When I Survey................... 191

Devotional

Amazing Grace 161
Break Thou the Bread......... 237
Come, Holy Spirit.............. 119
Come, Thou Fount.............. 190

Day Is Dying 130
Have Thine Own Way........... 253
He Leadeth Me 165
Holy, Holy, Holy.................... 126
How Sweet the Name.......... 187
I Need Thee Every Hour....... 173
Jesus, Lover of My Soul....... 118
Jesus, the Very Thought.... 214
My Faith Looks Up................ 198
My Jesus, I Love Thee 261
Near the Cross...................... 156
O Master, Let Me Walk....... 202
Something for Thee.............. 149
Sun of My Soul..................... 177
Sweet Hour of Prayer.......... 255

Duets

All on the Altar..................... 102
Beautiful Redeemer 13
Have Thine Own Way........... 253
In the Garden 277
My Jesus, I Love Thee........ 261
'Neath the Old Olive Trees.. 40
The Lord Is My Shepherd.... 67
The Old Rugged Cross........... 34

Evening Hymns

Abide With Me...................... 179
Day Is Dying........................ 130
Nearer My God To Thee.... 206
Near to the Heart................. 225
Softly Now the Light............ 263
Sun of My Soul..................... 177

Faith

All the Way My Saviour...... 290
Faith Is the Victory.............. 14
Faith of Our Fathers........... 201
Faith of Our Mothers........... 203
Have Faith in God................. 52
He Leadeth Me...................... 165
My Faith Looks Up................ 198
My Hope Is Built................... 22
O for a Faith......................... 269

Fellowship

All the Way My Saviour....... 290
Blest Be the Tie................... 218
In the Garden 277
Leaning on the Everlasting.. 268
O Master, Let Me Walk....... 202
Trust and Obey..................... 104
What a Friend....................... 160

Funeral

Abide With Me...................... 179
Beautiful River 192
I Must Tell Jesus................... 36
Lead Kindly Light................. 217
Nearer My God to Thee....... 206
O Love that Wilt Not........... 219
Rock of Ages......................... 264
Safe in the Arms of.............. 88
Sweet By and By................... 89
The Home Over There 79
When the Morning Comes.... 134

God

A Mighty Fortress................. 76
God Be With You................... 299
Guide Me, O Thou Great... 181
Holy, Holy, Holy.................... 126
O For a Thousand Tongues.. 125
O God, Our Help................... 193
There's a Wideness.............. 182
We Praise Thee, O God........ 163

Grace

Amazing Grace 161
Christ Receiveth Sinful Men 113
Come, Thou Fount................. 190
His Grace Is Sufficient......... 59
Majestic Sweetness 170
Pass Me Not......................... 224
There's a Wideness 182

Guidance

All the Way My Saviour........ 290
Footsteps of Jesus................. 222
Guide Me, O Thou Great..... 181
He Leadeth Me...................... 165
Jesus, Saviour, Pilot Me........ 176
Saviour, Like a Shepherd.... 57

Heaven

Beautiful River 192
On Jordan's Stormy Banks.. 283
Sweet By and By.................... 89
The Home Over There........... 79

Holy Spirit

Break Thou the Bread.......... 237
Breathe On Me...................... 275
Come, Holy Spirit................. 119
Come, Thou Almighty.......... 124
Fall Fresh on Me................... 229
Holy Ghost, with Light........ 204
Holy Spirit, Faithful............. 212
Seal Us, O Holy Spirit........ 207

Invitation

Almost Persuaded 183
Come, Sinner, Come............. 184
Come, Ye Sinners................. 223
His Way with Thee............... 136
I Am Praying for You........... 271
I Gave My Life for Thee....... 185
I Surrender All 103
Jesus, I Come....................... 69
Jesus Is Calling.................... 61
Just As I Am......................... 162
Let Him In............................ 71
Only Trust Him.................... 197
Softly and Tenderly.............. 100
Take My Life and Let........... 172
The Nail-Scarred Hand......... 39
There Is a Fountain............. 75
Where He Leads Me.............. 166
Wherever He Leads, I'll Go.. 99
Why Do You Wait?.............. 167

Jesus, Saviour

Alas! and Did My Saviour.... 211
Fairest Lord Jesus................ 215
He Keeps Me Singing........... 105
How Sweet the Name........... 187
Jesus, Lover of My Soul....... 118
Jesus Loves Even Me............ 273
Jesus Loves Me 243
Jesus Paid It All................... 194
Jesus Saves 5
Majestic Sweetness............... 170
My Jesus, I Love Thee.......... 261
My Redeemer 106
O Jesus, I Have Promised..... 195
Saviour, Like a Shepherd..... 57
Take the Name of Jesus....... 233
There is a Name................... 270
The Lily of the Valley.......... 45
'Tis Midnight 157
'Tis So Sweet to Trust.......... 249
Wonderful Jesus 35

Joy

He Keeps Me Singing........... 105
I Will Sing the Wondrous
  Story 280
Jesus Loves Even Me 273
Oh, How I Love Jesus........... 270
Sunshine In the Soul 109
We're Marching to Zion 11

Lord's Day

O Day of Rest and Gladness 129
Safely Through Another
  Week 128

Lord's Supper

Alas! and Did My Saviour.... 211
Blest Be the Tie................... 218
Bread of Heaven................... 220
I Gave My Life for Thee.... 185

In the Cross of Christ........... 180
Jesus, the Very Thought 214
My Jesus, I Love Thee.......... 261
When I Survey...................... 191

Love

I Love Him 153
Jesus Loves Even Me............ 273
Jesus Loves Me 243
Love Divine 4
Love is the Theme................. 114
Love Lifted Me 55
My Jesus, I Love Thee.......... 261
My Saviour's Love................. 21
Saviour, Thy Dying Love..... 149
Why Should He Love Me....... 46

Missionary Hymns

From Greenland's Icy
  Mountains 73
Jesus Saves 5
Jesus Shall Reign................. 150
Let the Lower Lights............. 265
O Zion Haste........................ 151
Rescue the Perishing.......... 19
Send the Light 117
The Kingdom is Coming....... 91
The Light of the World......... 230
The Morning Light is
  Breaking 56
Throw Out the Life-Line....... 18
We've a Story to Tell........... 7

Mother's Day Hymns

Faith of Our Mothers........... 203
My Mother's Bible................. 285

Opening Hymns

All Hail the Power.............120-121
All People that on................ 123
Come, Holy Spirit................. 119
Come, Thou Almighty.......... 124
Come, Thou Fount............... 190
Crown Him with Many......... 1
Holy, Holy, Holy................... 126
I Love Thy Kingdom............. 196
In Thy Holy Temple............. 288
O for a Thousand................. 125
O Worship the King.............. 122
Thy Holy Temple.................. 260
We Praise Thee O God......... 163
We're Marching to Zion...... 11

Patriotic

America 236
America the Beautiful........... 77
Faith of Our Fathers............. 201
Onward, Christian Soldiers.. 9

Praise

All Hail the Power.............120-121
Blessed Assurance 3
Come Thou Almighty............ 124
Fairest Lord Jesus................ 215
For the Beauty of................. 213
Glory to His Name................ 155
Holy, Holy, Holy................... 126
Joy to the World.................. 140
O Worship the King.............. 122
Praise Him, Praise Him........ 2
Revive Us Again.................... 163
When Morning Gilds............. 127

Prayer

Abide with Me...................... 179
Close to Thee........................175
Higher Ground 131
Holy Ghost with Light.......... 204
I am Thine, O Lord.............. 6
I Need Thee Every Hour....... 173
Jesus, Lover of My Soul....... 118
My Prayer 226
Near the Cross...................... 156
Nearer My God to Thee....... 206
Pass Me Not.......................... 224
Rock of Ages......................... 264
Saviour, Like a Shepherd.... 57
Speak to My Heart............... 93

Sweet Hour of Prayer............ 255
'Tis the Blessed Hour............ 43
What a Friend...................... 160
Whisper a Prayer................. 266

Quartets

All On the Altar.................. 102
Blessed Redeemer 41
Breathe On Me.................... 275
Holy Ghost with Light.......... 204
In Thy Holy Temple............. 288
Is Your All on the Altar 110
Near to the Heart of God.... 225
The Beautiful Garden............ 135
The Lord Is My Shepherd.... 67
The Old Rugged Cross 34
Why Should He Love Me So .. 46
Wonderful Peace of.............. 116
Wonderful Jesus 35

Repentance

Come, Humble Sinner............ 186
I Am Resolved..................... 20
I Surrender All................... 103
I Will Arise and Go.............. 223
Jesus, I Come...................... 69
Pass Me Not........................ 224

Resurrection

Christ Arose 139
Christ the Lord.................... 64
He Lives 48
He Lives on High.................. 83

Security

He Hideth My Soul............... 30
How Firm a Foundation........ 171
Leaning on the Everlasting.. 268
My Hope Is Built................. 22
Once for All 84
The Haven of Rest................ 272

Social Service

Am I a Soldier of................ 199
Give of Your Best................ 286
I Would Be Like Thee 282
I Would Be True.................. 289
Jesus Calls Us.................... 159
Let Others See Jesus............ 284
Make Me a Channel............... 27
Rescue the Perishing............ 19
Serve the Lord with Glad-
ness 137
Throw Out the Life-Line.... 18
To the Work........................ 53
Work for the Night Is
Coming 210

Solos

All On the Altar.................. 102
Beautiful Redeemer 13
Beneath the Cross................ 262
Breathe On Me..................... 275

I Will Not Forget Thee........ 274
I Would Be Like Thee............ 282
I Would Be True................... 289
In the Garden..................... 277
Is Your All on the Altar....... 110
Jesus My Lord Is Real......... 90
My Saviour First of All........ 291
My Mother's Bible.......... 285
Near to the Heart................ 225
'Neath the Old Olive Trees .. 40
Satisfied with Jesus............ 97
Seal Us, O Holy Spirit.......... 207
Speak to My Heart................ 93
The Beautiful Garden............ 135
The Lily of the Valley.......... 45
The Ninety and Nine............ 74
What Will You Do with
Jesus 101
When the Morning Comes.... 134
Wherever He Leads............... 99

Soul-Winning

Bring Them In..................... 251
Bringing in the Sheaves........ 281
Fall Fresh on Me.................. 229
I Am Praying for You........... 271
Jesus Calls Us 5
Lead Me to Some Soul 239
Let Others See Jesus............ 284
Lord, Lay Some Soul Upon.. 238
Make Me a Channel............... 27
Must I Go, and Empty........ 158
Rescue the Perishing............ 19
Revive Us Again................... 163
Revive Thy People................ 231
The Ninety and Nine............ 74
Throw Out the Life-Line........ 18

Stewardship

Give of Your Best................ 286
I Gave My Life for Thee 185
I Would be True.................. 289
Jesus Calls Us.................... 159
Make Me a Channel............... 27
O Master, Let Me Walk......... 202
O Zion, Haste 151
Our Best 87
Ready 164
Something for Thee 149
Take My Life and Let........... 172
Trust, Try and Prove Me.... 258

Temperance

America, the Beautiful............ 77
I Am Praying for You........... 271
Lead On, Lead On................. 293
Onward, Christian Soldiers.. 9
Rescue the Perishing............. 19
Stand Up for Jesus................ 8
Yield Not to Temptation........ 86

Trust

A Mighty Fortress.................. 76
Follow On 132
Have Thine Own Way........... 253

Jesus, Lover of My.............. 118
Leaning on the Everlasting.. 268
O Love that Wilt Not........... 219
Only Trust Him................... 197
'Tis So Sweet to Trust 249
Trusting Jesus 228

Warning

Almost Persuaded 183
Come, Humble Sinner........... 186
Come, Sinner, Come.............. 184
There's a Great Day............. 209
What Will You Do with 101
Why Do You Wait................. 167
Ye Must Be Born Again........ 38

Worship

Aids to Worship.................300-314
All Hail the Power.............120-121
Come, Thou Almighty........... 124
Crown Him with Many 1
Day is Dying in the West.... 130
For the Beauty of................ 213
Hark! the Herald Angels.... 142
Holy, Holy, Holy................. 126
In Thy Holy Temple............. 288
O Come All Ye Faithful 143
O Day of Rest and Gladness 129
O for a Thousand.................. 125
O God Our Help 193
O Worship the King............. 122
Praise Him, Praise Him....... 2
When Morning Gilds............. 127

Youth Hymns

Breathe on Me..................... 275
Fairest Lord Jesus............... 215
Faith of Our Fathers............. 201
Fall Fresh on Me.................. 229
Follow the Living Christ..... 234
Give of Your Best................ 286
Have Faith in God.............. 52
Have Thine Own Way........... 253
He Lives 48
I Would be True................... 289
In Thy Holy Temple............. 288
Jesus Shall Reign................. 150
Lead Me to Some Soul......... 239
Living for Jesus................... 96
'Neath the Old Olive Trees.... 40
O Jesus, I Have Promised..... 195
O Master, Let Me Walk........ 202
Onward, Christian Soldiers .. 9
Our Best 87
Satisfied with Jesus............ 97
Saved, Saved 44
Serve the Lord with........... 137
Silent Night 146
Take Time to Be Holy.......... 15
The Banner of the Cross.... 10
The Lily of the Valley.......... 45
Thy Word Have I Hid........... 107
When I Survey.......... 191
Wherever He Leads............... 99
Whisper a Prayer................. 266
Yield Not to Temptation....... 86

INDEX

Titles are in SMALL CAPS; first lines in lower-case type

A

A FRIEND OF MINE...... 95
A MIGHTY FORTRESS.... 76
A ruler once came.... 38
A wonderful Saviour.. 30
ABIDE WITH ME........ 179
ABLE, WILLING, MIGHTY. 63
ALAS! AND DID......... 211
Alas! and did
   (Hudson) 112
All hail the power..120-121
ALL ON THE ALTAR.... 102
ALL PEOPLE THAT ON... 123
ALL THE WAY MY...... 290
ALL THINGS COME OF .. 309
All to Jesus I........ 103
ALMOST PERSUADED..... 183
AM I A SOLDIER?....... 199
AMAZING GRACE........ 161
AMENS 310-314
AMERICA 236
AMERICA THE BEAUTI-
  FUL 77
ANGELS, FROM THE..... 145
ANYWHERE WITH JESUS 16
ARE YOU WASHED IN... 111
AT THE CROSS.......... 112
AT THE ROLL CALL...... 78

B

Be silent.............. 305
Beautful garden of.... 135
BEAUTIFUL REDEEMER... 13
BEAUTIFUL RIVER....... 192
BENEATH THE CROSS.... 262
BLESS THE LORD........ 306
BLESS THOU THE GIFTS 308
BLESSED ASSURANCE.... 3
BLESSED REDEEMER...... 41
BLEST BE THE TIE...... 218
BREAD OF HEAVEN...... 220
BREAK THOU THE....... 237
BREATHE ON ME........ 275
Brightly beams our.... 265
BRING THEM IN........ 251
Bring ye all the........ 258
BRINGING IN THE
  SHEAVES 281
BY THE WAY OF
  THE CROSS........... 278

C

CALLING THE PRODIGAL.. 250
CHILD'S MORNING HYMN 240
CHRIST AROSE.......... 139
CHRIST RECEIVETH...... 113
CHRIST THE LORD IS.... 64
Christ the Saviour..... 83
CLOSE TO THEE......... 175
Come every soul....... 197
COME, HOLY SPIRIT,..... 119
COME, HUMBLE SINNER. 186
COME, SINNER, COME... 184
COME, THOU ALMIGHTY. 124
COME, THOU FOUNT.... 190
Come, we that love.... 112
Come, ye sinners...... 223
COUNT YOUR BLESSINGS 248
CROWN HIM WITH..... 1

D

DAY IS DYING IN THE.. 130
Down at the cross...... 155
Down in the valley.... 132
DOXOLOGY 300

E

Encamped along the... 14
Every Sunday evening. 246

F

FADE, FADE, EACH...... 205
FAIREST LORD JESUS.... 215
FAITH IS THE VICTORY.. 14
FAITH OF OUR FATHERS. 201
FAITH OF OUR MOTHERS 203
FALL FRESH ON ME.... 229
Father, we thank...... 240
FLING OUT THE BANNER 152
FOLLOW ON............. 132
FOLLOW THE LIVING.... 234
FOOTSTEPS OF JESUS.... 222
For God so loved...... 232
FOR THE BEAUTY OF.... 213
Free from the law.... 84
From all the dark...... 91
FROM EVERY STORMY.... 189
FROM GREENLAND'S..... 73

G

GIVE OF YOUR BEST..... 286
GLORIOUS IS THY NAME 292
GLORY TO HIS NAME... 155

God be with you...... 299
God is calling the...... 250
GOLDEN PALACES....... 259
Gone from my heart.. 153
GOOD MORNING TO YOU.. 244
GUIDE ME, O THOU..... 181

H

HALLELUJAH FOR THE.. 297
HARK, HARK, MY SOUL. 32
HARK! THE HERALD.... 142
Hark, 'tis the........ 251
HAVE FAITH IN GOD.... 52
HAVE I GRIEVED THY... 276
HAVE THINE OWN WAY. 253
Have you been to..... 111
Have you failed in.... 39
HEAR OUR PRAYER..... 307
Hear ye the Master's.. 87
HE HIDETH MY SOUL... 30
HE INCLUDED ME....... 31
HE IS ABLE TO DELIVER.. 94
HE IS COMING........ 298
HE KEEPS ME SINGING.. 105
HE LEADETH ME....... 165
HE LIVES.............. 48
HE LIVES ON HIGH..... 83
HE RANSOMED ME...... 254
HIGHER GROUND....... 131
HIS GRACE IS.......... 59
HIS LOVE WON MY..... 47
HIS WAY WITH THEE... 136
HOLY BIBLE, BOOK...... 216
HOLY GHOST WITH.... 204
HOLY, HOLY, HOLY..... 126
HOLY SPIRIT, BREATHE.. 275
HOLY SPIRIT, FAITHFUL 212
How firm a........... 171
HOW SWEET THE NAME 187

I

I am happy today.... 50
I AM PRAYING FOR..... 271
I AM RESOLVED......... 20
I am satisfied........ 97
I am so glad.......... 273
I am so happy in..... 31
I AM THINE, O LORD.... 6
I can hear my....... 166
I come to thee........ 277
I GAVE MY LIFE FOR.... 185
I have found a friend.. 45
I hear the Saviour.... 194

I heard the bells...... 148
I KNOW THE BIBLE IS... 68
I KNOW WHOM I HAVE.. 29
I LOVE HIM........... 153
I LOVE THY KINGDOM.. 196
I LOVE TO TELL THE.... 25
I MUST TELL JESUS.... 36
I NEED THEE EVERY.... 173
I serve a risen........ 48
I SHALL NOT LIVE IN.. 256
I stand amazed....... 21
I SURRENDER ALL....... 103
I want my life to...... 62
I WAS GLAD WHEN...... 245
I was sinking deep.... 55
I was sinking down.. 92
I WILL ARISE AND GO.... 223
I will look for you.... 78
I WILL NOT FORGET THEE 274
I will sing of my...... 106
I will sing the........ 280
I wandered in the.... 279
I WON'T HAVE TO CROSS. 54
I WOULD BE LIKE THEE.. 282
I WOULD BE TRUE...... 289
I'm pressing on the... 131
IN THE CROSS OF CHRIST 180
IN THE GARDEN........ 277
IN THY HOLY TEMPLE.. 288
IS YOUR ALL ON THE... 110
Is your life a channel.. 27
IT CAME UPON THE.... 141
IT IS WELL WITH...... 33
I'VE FOUND A FRIEND... 70

J

JESUS CALLS US....... 159
JESUS, I COME......... 69
JESUS, I MY CROSS..... 72
Jesus is able to save.. 63
JESUS IS CALLING...... 61
Jesus is standing..... 101
Jesus, keep me near... 156
JESUS LIFTED ME...... 92
JESUS, LOVER OF MY... 118
JESUS LOVES EVEN ME.. 273
JESUS LOVES ME........ 243
JESUS LOVES THE LITTLE 241
JESUS MY LORD IS REAL 90
JESUS PAID IT ALL...... 194
JESUS SAVES........... 5
JESUS, SAVIOUR, PILOT.. 176
JESUS SHALL REIGN..... 150
JESUS! THE VERY...... 214
JOHN THREE SIXTEEN... 232
JOY TO THE WORLD..... 140
JUST AS I AM.......... 162

L

LEAD, KINDLY LIGHT... 217
LEAD ME TO SOME SOUL 239
LEAD ON, LEAD ON...... 293

LEAD ON, O KING...... 200
LEANING ON THE....... 268
LET HIM IN........... 71
LET OTHERS SEE JESUS. 284
LET THE LOWER LIGHTS.. 265
LET THE TIDE COME IN.. 60
LIVING FOR JESUS...... 96
LOOK AND LIVE........ 168
LORD, LAY SOME SOUL.. 238
LOVE DIVINE........... 4
LOVE IS THE THEME.... 114
LOVE LIFTED ME........ 55
Low in the grave He.. 139

M

MAJESTIC SWEETNESS... 170
MAKE ME A CHANNEL.. 27
Master the tempest.... 296
MORE ABOUT JESUS.... 169
More holiness give.... 226
MORE LOVE TO THEE.. 227
MUST I GO AND........ 158
MUST JESUS BEAR THE.. 154
My country 'tis of.... 236
MY DESIRE............. 62
MY FAITH LOOKS UP.. 198
My hope is built...... 22
MY JESUS, AS THOU... 178
MY JESUS, I LOVE THEE. 261
MY MOTHER'S BIBLE.... 285
MY PRAYER............ 226
MY REDEEMER........ 106
MY SAVIOUR FIRST...... 291
MY SAVIOUR'S LOVE... 21
MY SOUL, BE ON....... 174
My soul in sad exile.. 272

N

NEAR THE CROSS....... 156
NEAR TO THE HEART.... 225
NEARER, MY GOD, TO.... 206
'NEATH THE OLD OLIVE.. 40
No LONGER LONELY..... 82
NOT ALL THE BLOOD..... 208
NOTHING BUT THE...... 188

O

O beautiful for........ 77
O COME, ALL YE........ 143
O DAY OF REST AND.... 129
O FOR A FAITH......... 269
O FOR A THOUSAND.... 125
O GOD, OUR HELP...... 193
O HAPPY DAY.......... 294
O HOLY NIGHT......... 295
O how I love........ 270
O JESUS, I HAVE....... 195
O LITTLE TOWN OF...... 144
O LOVE THAT WILT NOT. 219
O MASTER, LET ME WALK 202
O think of the home.. 79
O WORSHIP THE KING.. 122

O ZION, HASTE......... 151
Of Jesus' love that.... 12
Of the themes that.... 114
On a hill far away.... 34
On a hill lone and.... 278
ON JORDAN'S STORMY.. 283
ONCE FOR ALL......... 84
ONE DAY.............. 28
ONLY TRUST HIM...... 197
ONWARD, CHRISTIAN.... 9
OUR BEST.............. 87
Out of my bondage..... 69
Out of the golden..... 259

P

PASS ME NOT.......... 224
PEACE! BE STILL........ 296
POWER IN THE BLOOD... 85
PRAISE GOD FROM...... 300
PRAISE HIM, ALL YE... 242
PRAISE HIM, PRAISE HIM 2
PRAYER CHANGES....... 58
PRAYER RESPONSE...... 247

R

READY 164
REJOICE 49
RESCUE THE PERISHING 19
REVIVE THY PEOPLE.... 231
REVIVE US AGAIN...... 163
ROCK OF AGES.......... 264

S

SAFE IN THE ARMS OF.. 88
SAFELY THROUGH...... 128
SATISFIED WITH JESUS.. 97
SAVED, SAVED!........ 44
SAVIOUR, LIKE A....... 57
SAVIOUR, MORE THAN.. 235
Saviour thy dying...... 149
SEAL US, O HOLY....... 207
SEND THE LIGHT....... 117
SERVE THE LORD WITH.. 137
Shall we gather........ 192
SILENT NIGHT........ 146
Simply trusting....... 228
Sing them over again.. 221
Sinners Jesus will..... 113
SOFTLY AND TENDERLY.. 100
SOFTLY NOW THE LIGHT 263
SOMETHING FOR JESUS.. 149
Sowing in the......... 281
SPEAK TO MY HEART.. 93
Spirit of the living.... 229
STAND UP, STAND UP... 8
STANDING ON THE..... 17
STEPPING IN THE LIGHT 81
SUN OF MY SOUL...... 177
SUNLIGHT 279
SUNSHINE IN THE SOUL. 109
SWEET BY AND BY...... 89
SWEET HOUR OF PRAYER 255
Sweet is the promise.. 274

Sweet peace, the gift	42	There is a name I love 270	What a fellowship.... 268
Sweeter as the years	12	There is never a day.... 35	What a friend....... 160
Sweetly Lord, Have We	222	There is a place of.... 225	What can wash away.. 188

T

Take my life, and let	172	There shall be....... 23	What will you do 101
Take the name of...	233	There were ninety.... 74	When I survey....... 191
Take time to be holy.	15	There's a call comes.. 117	When Jesus comes.... 37
Take up thy cross......	99	There's a garden...... 135	When morning gilds. 127
Tell me the old, old..	24	There's a great day.. 209	When peace like a.... 33
Thanks be to God....	108	There's a land that.... 89	When the morning... 134
That will be glory..	51	There's a royal........ 10	When the roll is.... 252
The church's one....	66	There's a stranger at.. 71	When we walk with.. 104
The cross, it standeth..	297	There's a wideness.. 182	Where he leads me... 166
The banner of the...	10	There's within my..... 105	Wherever he leads.... 99
The beautiful garden	135	Thou my everlasting.. 175	While Jesus whispers.. 184
The great physician.	267	Throw out life-line.. 18	While passing.......... 284
The happy story hour	246	Thy holy temple.... 260	While shepherds..... 147
The haven of rest...	272	Thy word have i hid. 107	Whisper a prayer..... 266
The home over there.	79	Thy word is a lamp.... 107	Whosoever heareth.... 138
The kingdom is	91	'Tis midnight......... 157	Whosoever meaneth
The light of the.....	230	'Tis so sweet to trust. 249	me 50
The lily of the valley	45	'Tis the blessed hour. 43	Whosoever will...... 138
The Lord is in his...	301	To the work........ 53	Why do you wait?.... 167
The Lord is my.......	67	Tread softly......... 305	Why should he love.. 46
The morning light is	56	Trials dark on........ 134	Will Jesus find us... 37
The nail-scarred hand	39	Trust and obey...... 104	Wonderful Jesus..... 35
The never-failing		Trust, try, and prove. 258	Wonderful man of.... 115
hand	133	Trusting Jesus....... 228	Wonderful peace of.. 116
The ninety and nine	74	Trying to walk........ 81	Wonderful words of.. 221
The old rugged cross.	34		Work for the night.. 210
The rainbow with....	257	**U**	Would you live for.... 136
The shepherd of love	26	Up calvary's mountain.. 41	
The solid rock........	22		**Y**
The son of God goes..	65	**W**	Ye must be born...... 38
The whole world was..	230	We have heard the.... 5	Yield not to.......... 86
There comes to my....	42	We praise thee, O God.. 163	You have longed....... 110
There is a fountain..	75	We shall see the king 80	
There is a green hill	98	We're marching to... 11	**Z**
		We've a story to tell. 7	Zion stands with..... 287